Liz Lives

Healed with God's Word and His Food

BONUS: Twenty Near-Keto Recipes included!

Elizabeth 'Liz' Soldahl

Liz Lives:
Healed with God's Word and Food
Copyright © 2020 Elizabeth Soldahl
Dovestar Publishing International
7149 Highway 11, Box #42 Sunset, SC 29685-9998

ISBN- 978-1-7320246-8-7
ISBN- 1732024685

Cover photo taken at Hendry's Beach, in Santa Barbara by Eric Soldahl

Heartfelt Disclaimer:

My intent is not to dispense medical advice. Our greatest resource of all is the *Greatest Physician of All*—our God and Creator.

My biggest encouragement to you dear reader, is that you take responsibility for your own health. To allow your body to heal and stay whole in the way it was designed. Turning to God and His Word—*His food*—for your health and well-being. Considering we are in partnership with God, how can we do our part caring for our bodies with HIS food? It is both edible and found in His Holy Word.

Contact information:
elizabethsoldahl@yahoo.com
Website: www.faithonfire.net

Order Books on Amazon.com

Health/Faith/Christian Living/Inspirational $9.95 US

Contents

Preface

With Liz Lives, discover God's prescription to healing and health.
God provides us the remedy through His Word and His Food.

As a three-time cancer survivor, sometimes I feel like I am walking on eggshells, waiting for the fourth shoe to drop. But as I have been penning this book, reflecting on all of the healing and miracles in my life and those around me, and studying God's promises, things changed. My Born-Again Christian Faith grew stronger and the Holy Spirit re-ignited within me. I realized that FAITH is not a Feeling…. In fact Faith is active; it is Believing God's Promises.

You, dear reader can tap into this amazing gift of Healing Faith as well. With the help of God we can clear the stumbling blocks that may hinder our healing, including issues with food, doubt, unforgiveness, demonic strongholds and unhealthy thoughts. My hope and prayer is that, by the grace of God, your faith and health will be strengthened and fortified; completely RENEWED!

I offer up this book with the utmost love, tenderness and compassion. May you live an abundant life with great health and most of all receive God's promise of life everlasting!

With Jesus' love and healing for all,
Elizabeth (Liz)

Note: I felt called by God to share the information and stories in this book. It has been a challenging but enlightening journey. Some ideas presented may stir up strong feelings within you. I humbly ask that you press on, gleaning pearls of wisdom that apply to you.

I have discovered that **truth** is often neglected today's world. I hope you will read this with a soft open heart and open mind.

Dedication

My life is dedicated to God for His constant love, healing and forgiveness. By His grace I was delivered into freedom.
My story is dedicated to my devoted husband, Eric Soldahl, who stood by my side in sickness and in health.
My Special Thanks to Laura Tate Anderson for her endless hours of expert editing, wise counsel and friendship!

Favorite Healing Verses:
"I shall not die, but live, and declare the works of the Lord!" (Psalm 118:17)

"I will restore your health, and heal your wounds." (Jeremiah 30:17)

Jesus said: "Because I live, ye shall live also." (John 14:19)

"Confess your faults to one another, and pray for one another that ye may be healed." (James 5:16)

"Thy word is a Lamp unto my feet and a light unto my path." (Psalm 119:105)

"By His Stripes I am healed" (Isaiah 53)

"Praise the Lord, oh my soul, and forget not all His benefits-Who *forgives* all your sins and *heals* all your diseases..." (Psalm 103:3)

Jesus said, "Daughter, your faith has made you whole. Go in peace and be healed of your disease." (Mark 5:34)

"The doctor of the future will give no medicine but will interest his patients in their care of the human frame, in diet, and the cause and prevention of disease." Thomas Edison

Listening to God's Voice

"In my trouble, I cried to the Lord and He answered me."
— Psalm 120:1

Often, I have cried out to the Lord. The times I have called out the loudest perhaps, was when faced with cancer. Not once, not twice, but three times.

My first brush with cancer was in 2002 when God delivered me from colon cancer. Twelve inches of my lower intestines were removed. In 2004 a melanoma mole was sliced from my arm. And in March of 2014 I endured a double mastectomy. Seven cancerous tumors were removed along with both of my breasts.

I chose to have all three cancers removed through surgery.

I prayerfully decided not to do chemotherapy, radiation, or pharmaceutical drugs. Strange as it sounds, I am grateful for those three cancers. It forced me to grow closer to God, prompted me to research healthy life strategies, and gave me a message to share.

As you comb through the pages of this book, I hope you will be encouraged on your journey by the way God provides healing. May His Word, His food and His 'Still, Small Voice' speak to you directly.

Prayer over Pressure

An earlier time in my own life while battling cancer I did not hear God's voice so easily at first.

The doctor's voice was clear on the phone "I have news from the biopsies. I am very sorry to have to tell you Elizabeth, it is invasive breast cancer, seven tumors....."

Hearing that I had cancer, my body started shaking.

After hanging up the phone I cried and cried as I lay on the floor. My husband, Eric, kneeled down beside me and kissed my cheek. When there were no tears left, I breathed deeply, and in that moment, I realized that I was not alone. God was with me, and my husband was with me too.

Although I knew I was not alone, I was overwhelmed by all of the options presented to me through research, doctors and well-meaning friends and family. I felt pressure. Pressure to move fast.

I awoke before sunrise one morning, and cried out to God in prayer:

"Help me, Lord! The doctors want me to do surgery, chemo, radiation, and hormonal replacement drugs. The surgeon needs to know my decision by next Friday, and I have already cancelled the surgery twice!

Oh God, I remember the woman in the Bible with the issue of bleeding who spent all of her money on physicians and, grew worse, not better. Then she was healed by You, Jesus. Please, Lord, make it clear what you want me to do. Thank you, Lord, Amen!"

I pleaded this prayer for days.

I had one day left to notify the hospital if I wanted to cancel the scheduled double mastectomy surgery. That critical morning, as I lay in bed next to my husband, I heard a powerful message. It echoed through my heart and mind; I believed it was the spirit of God speaking to me:

"I will heal you though the surgery. I will heal you through the surgery."

I remember asking God,

"Are you sure?" and the message reverberated through my whole being:

"I will heal you through the surgery."

Then I woke Eric up suddenly.

"God is going to heal me through the surgery!" I exclaimed.

The next thing that happened seemed to confirm that surgery would cut out the cancerous tumors *by the root* and heal me.

Every morning, I prepared a glass of warm water with fresh lemon juice, honey and apple cider vinegar. This was a remedy I learned from a long-term cancer survivor that had decided against conventional treatment.

As I cut the lemon that morning, I noticed a half inch brownish-black ugly growth on the side of the lemon. With a razor-sharp paring knife, I sliced off that end of the lemon. The rest of the lemon was fresh and juicy, in pristine condition. *Could that bad spot on the lemon be like the abnormal lumps in my breasts? Would the tumors be cut off as easily, leaving the rest of my body clean and free of the disease?*

Then during my morning devotional meditation time, I read:

"For I will restore your health and heal your wounds says the Lord" (Jeremiah 30:17) ...*another confirmation, my heart leaped, I would be healed by God.*

And in fact, I *was* Healed by God.

A New Lump

It had been four years since my double mastectomy surgery and complete healing. Once again, I found myself struck with fear. There was a golf size ball lump on the right side of my spine. After research, my concern grew. Because of my "Spirit of Infirmity," I was convinced there was another cancer. I scheduled a doctor's appointment that was followed up with an ultrasound. Before the ultrasound, I was swimming alone in a hotel pool and found myself praying to God once again.

"Please help me Lord, please help me...I am scared God. What is going on? Help me Lord Jesus, I need you. What shall I do?"

Then I heard a still small voice in my heart. It was from God: *"It is My Word and My food."*

Okay Lord, you healed me through the surgery with my breast disease, now I will trust you again...and God, what exactly do you mean by, 'My Word and My food'?

Again I heard the still small voice:

"I will heal you through My Word and My food."

After my swim I started to do some more research on healing foods. The Ketogenic and Plant Based diets kept popping up on my screen. The research revealed that through our food and fasting, we can starve cancer. This confirmed my previous research and lifestyle changes I had already begun implementing.

I went to the ultrasound a few days later and my technician Sarah shared with me about her great healing with her osteoporosis and I shared with her my fears about the golf ball size lump in my back as well as the Word of God that I got in the swimming pool. The clinician's eyes lit up and she explained;

"God's Word is God's food! It has a double meaning." She said, "Don't believe any negative *reports* from the doctors, believe in God's Report. God's report is what He promises in the Bible. He healed me and He can heal you too."

She asked sweetly, "May I pray for you Elizabeth, right now?" Then she held my hand and said, "Lord I lift up Elizabeth to you. Lord You say in Your Word that if two people are gathered together and are in agreement, they can ask anything in the name of the Lord Jesus and it will be granted. So we are asking for complete healing for Elizabeth. Thank You Lord for Your healing. In Jesus name. Amen."

I received my results from the ultrasound a week later and the golf ball on my spine turned out to be just a muscle knot from my slight scoliosis. However the ultrasound did reveal a half inch bright spot on my left kidney. The Radiologist suggested further testing on the kidney. I prayed with my husband Eric and felt the clear conviction that God would heal me through His food; both His physical food and His Word.

It's been several years since that ultrasound, and I continue to sleep peacefully at night believing in God's Promises. I did not return for further testing or ultrasounds, and *closed the door* on any doubts. I chose to rely on God's Word and His Food for physical and spiritual sustenance.

How to Hear His Voice

Nita Hanson is a Missionary friend of ours to the country of Ukraine. She ministers to needy disabled children and families by obtaining wheelchairs for them and sharing Jesus.

As a Missionary, Nita often speaks to large church groups when visiting the United States. She shares how we can **ALL** hear God's voice. It takes patience, discernment and prayer.

To hear God's voice clearly, we may need to remove personal "roadblocks". Scripture says, if we have 'iniquity' in our hearts, God cannot hear us. We will discuss removing roadblocks to healing in Chapter 10, called *Healing Defined*.

Twenty years ago, Nita heard a voice from God, to sell everything and move to the Ukraine near Russia. Her calling was to care for the impoverished in this war-torn country.

One Sunday, Nita explained that we can **train our ear and heart to hear His voice**. We can pray and ask for God's wisdom and guidance. We can read His precious Living Word, the Bible.

God says, "If you need wisdom, ask our generous God, and He will give it to you." Nita explained that it is a process and that over time we can learn to hear His *Still Small Voice*. When God speaks it is clear, concise, and brings you peace.

Scripture says, "My sheep hear My voice; I know them, and they follow Me."

Truly what we are listening for is the voice and promptings of the Holy Spirit that lives within us.

Often times there will be confirmations from other people and situations that help clarify and punctuate His message. Remember the ultrasound technician who prayed with me and told me, "God's Word is His Food...it has a double meaning." That was a huge confirmation for me. We can ask God for confirmations and clarity.

It is often important to **give medical decisions time**. Patience is a virtue. The devil wants to rush us. Doctors and well-meaning family and friends may pressure us to jump in with medical treatments. One of my friends prays and waits **30 days**, after hearing from God, before her final decision.

As humans, we want answers from God right away. But that is not how God works. He is not a genie in a bottle. He wants a relationship with us. He doesn't want rules or religion. God wants us to turn to Him with our sorrows, our joys, our requests, and our gratitude. Jesus wants to be our best friend. God sees the big picture and cares about all the details. Remember, in Romans 8:28 we are assured that:

"All things work together for good to those who love God, to those who are called according to His purpose."

The more we pay attention to God's word, and the more we act on His promptings, the more we will hear His voice. And God will never tell us something that goes against His Word in the Bible.

Jesus First Strategy:
"God will never tell us something that goes against His Word in the Bible."

I often seek Christian Counseling for guidance as well. Proverbs 11:14 says there is safety in a multitude of counselors. Yet at the end of the day, it is me and God making the decisions. We're a team.

For me, one of the most important ways to get close to God is through a 20 minute prayer/meditation time. My goal is to spend time with Him each morning reflecting on a Bible verse of the day. I started this practice over 20 years ago when my children were little and life was hectic. One friend asked me, "What are the 3 most important things to start your day?"

I replied, "First I say a prayer with my husband, then read a Bible verse. Then I meditate on that verse for 20 minutes." Joshua 1:8 says, *"Study this book (The Bible)... **meditate on it day and night.**"*

Prayer—Meditation and Journaling

Sitting quietly with Jesus in the morning for 20 minutes focusing on scripture brings me a peace that guides my whole day. The Holy Spirit gives guidance as a result of spending time with God. I encourage you to spend time with God and have a relationship with Him. Listen for, *"That still small voice."* Jesus meditated, so let's follow His example. I like to follow up my prayer/meditation time with journaling. It is so amazing to look back at old journals and see ALL the answered prayers! On the days I don't meditate my husband says he can tell a difference... and so can I.

Eight *Jesus First Strategies* to discern if you are hearing God's voice or that of the enemy:

1. God's voice will convict you in love: whereas the enemy's voice brings guilt and condemnation.
2. God's voice will encourage and reassure: whereas the enemy's voice will discourage and frighten.
3. God's voice will lead, guide and still: whereas <u>the enemy will push and RUSH.</u>
4. God's voice is calming: whereas the enemy makes us obsess and worry.
5. God's voice will bring comfort and peace: whereas the enemy's voice brings chaos and compromise.
6. God's voice brings clarity and confirmation: whereas the enemy's voice brings confusion and clouded conscience.
7. God's voice draws Christ closer to us: whereas the enemy's voice brings controlling spirits.
8. God's voice will always line up with His Word in the Bible: whereas the enemy will try to twist His words.

The Bible tells us in 1 Kings Chapter 19 that God reveals Himself to His prophet Elijah. There was a great strong wind that tore into the mountains, but the Lord was not in the wind. After the wind there was an earthquake, but the Lord was not in the earthquake. After the earthquake a fire, but the Lord was not in the fire. After the fire, there was a still small voice. That *still small voice* was the voice of God.

My Prayer: *"Thank you God for Your love and friendship. Forgive me for my sloth and distractions and not reading Your Word and praying more consistently! Help me to structure my time to spend more with You to hear only* **Your voice for direction and guidance***. I love you!"*

Love Your Daughter, Liz

Your Prayer and Reflection: What can you do in your own life to hear God's voice more clearly?

_____

_____

_____

The Great Physician
Understanding God's Character

"For I am the Lord who heals you."—*Exodus 15:26*

On the afternoon of my 57th birthday, I found out the truth of my life's beginning. We had just returned to my hometown of Santa Barbara, on the West Coast. My husband had planned a special dinner with my parents to celebrate. Now as I sat overlooking the peaceful Pacific Ocean, inside I was simmering...with my blood pressure rising. I had just heard the story of my birth—the true story.

Throughout my life, I had been told that after my birth the doctor thought I was a "Mongoloid Child." A younger resident doctor had diagnosed me with Down Syndrome based upon a set of wide eyes and low Apgar Score.

Now at dinner, the truth was finally revealed by my parents. My birth itself almost never happened. The story unfolded:

'A spinal block epidural had made my mother's blood pressure drop to near death. The needle had punctured through her spinal cord directly into the surrounding tissue and bloodstream. The devil was trying to kill my mother...and me from before my first breath. His weapon: a strong drug; one that dulls pain.

At that point, my Dad—a doctor himself—interceded saying, "Get my wife some adrenaline before she dies!"
It served to keep her heart pumping...and mine too.

Immediately after I was delivered, a resident doctor bolted into the delivery room, "Dr. Logan, I have good news and bad news. You have the girl you were hoping for, since you already have two sons; however, I think your baby girl has Down Syndrome. Her Apgar Mortality Score is way below normal." I needed resuscitation.

The day after my birth, September 21st 1961, the seasoned general pediatrician came in on rounds through the hospital and after further testing said I was okay after all. The Apgar reading had normalized, and... no Down Syndrome. He also admitted that the young doctor had pushed the epidural needle in too far, nearly causing both of our hearts to stop.

With my birth, the devil tried to take me out before I came into the world, but God had other plans; I was injected with a burning desire for truth and a fire in my heart to share it.

God is the Ultimate Physician

Does the Bible say:

"Are any among you sick?... then go to the doctor?"

No. The Bible says,

"Call for the elders of the church and pray over him anointing him with oil in the name of the Lord. And the prayer of faith will save the sick, and the Lord will raise him up." (James 5:14-15)

And Exodus 15 says, *"I am the Lord who heals you."*

Doctors can stitch you up, and cut out a lump, but only God can heal. It is not realistic or fair to expect doctors to heal like God. I recently read a startling statistic in WebMD that doctors' suicide rate is the highest of any profession. It's double that of the general population. I have much empathy for doctors because they are under such tremendous pressure. Have we made doctors our god? *God created doctors, but not to replace Him.*

Jesus First Strategy: "God created doctors, but *not* to replace Him."

I have great respect for doctors, and in fact I grew up in a family where my Dad was a physician, an Endocrinologist, and my brother is a practicing Dermatologist. Interestingly, a few years ago my brother, Mark, the Dermatologist, went to Asia and came home with a lot of natural eastern healing remedies. This inspired me to dig deeper into holistic cures.

God is our Jehovah Rapha, our Great Physician. The Bible teaches that it is in our best interest to turn to Him.

In 2ⁿᵈ Chronicles 16, there is a story about King Asa that enlightens us on this point.

King Asa had followed the Lord for many years and found great favor and won great battles.

*"For the eyes of the Lord run to and fro throughout the whole earth, to **show Himself strong** on behalf of those whose heart is loyal to Him."*

Then, King Asa started to look to others for guidance rather than the Lord. He was sternly warned by an advisor to turn back to God. Instead he became angry, placing the prophet in prison.

*"And in the thirty-ninth year of his reign, Asa became diseased in his feet, and his malady was severe. **Yet in his disease he did not seek the Lord, but the physicians.**"* King Asa died shortly thereafter...

This story illustrates how God wants us to turn to Him first...and there may consequences if we don't.

Attributes of God

-**God is Love:** *"For God so loved the world that He gave His only Son, whoever believes in Him should not perish but have everlasting life."* (John 3:16) *"I pray that you...will grasp how wide, long, high and deep is the love of Christ."* (Eph. 3:17-18) God loves you, God loves you, God loves you!
-**God is Jehovah Rapha our Great Physician/Healer:** In Exodus 15 God called Himself Jehovah-Rapha which in Hebrew means, "I am the Lord who heals you."

-**God is Everlasting:** *"I'm with you always even unto the end of the age."* (Matthew 28:20)

-**God is Omnipotent: He is All Powerful:** *"By the Word of the Lord the Heavens were made."* (Psalm 33:6)

-**God is Omniscient: He is All Knowing:** *"I am God and there is no other... I make known the end from the beginning."* (Isaiah 46:9-10)

-**God is Omnipresent: He is Always Everywhere:** *"Where can I go from your Spirit... if I ascend to Heaven you are there... if I dwell in the sea even there Your hand will lead me."* (Psalm 139:7-10)

-**God is a Jealous God:** He loves us so much, He does not want us to fall into the trap of worshipping false gods, that eventually ensnare us and take us down (Read the 1st commandment).

-**God is Faithful and Trustworthy:** *"The Lord God is a faithful God, keeping His covenant of love to a thousand generations...* (Deuteronomy 7:9) We can depend on Him.

-**God is Fair and Just:** His Justice will prevail. He will correct the misdirected, and sends us in the right direction with mercy. (Psalm 25:8)

Not only does God have all of these great attributes and more, but did you know that Jesus (who is God in flesh) healed every person who came to Him with **faith**? And He has continued to do so for over 2000 years. Hebrews 13:8 says,

"God is the same yesterday, today, and forever."

My Prayer: *"Dear God, thank You for Your awesome character! Thank you for allowing me to survive my birth. You are Just, Loving, Healer, Great Physician. Forgive me for sometimes forgetting who You are, and often assigning other people that role. I now declare You as my Healer, my Best Friend, my Loving Father. I love You and praise You for the continual healing in my life."*

Love, Your Daughter, Liz

Your Prayer and Reflection: Who do you trust as your Physician? How can you increase your trust in God as Healer?

_____

_____

_____

Faith Activates God's Power

Jesus says ten times in the Bible,
"Your faith has made you whole."

Our dear friends Pastor Rich and Karen Eddy invited me and my husband, Eric, for dinner a couple nights before my breast cancer surgery. They had a visitor staying with them from Ohio, Pastor Curtis Leins. His wife had survived breast cancer several years before.

I will never forget what happened after we ate our delicious chicken dinner. With Pastor Curtis on guitar and Eric on piano, we began a spontaneous spirit filled worship together. Then, everyone laid hands upon me, praying for a successful surgery and healing. The Holy Spirit was ever present in that circle.

Pastor Curtis looked at me intently and said, "Dear Elizabeth, I pray *'faith'* over you. I pray that you have faith in God to get you through this. **Faith** that you will be healed. Breathe, Elizabeth—Breathe Faith... *Faith, Faith, Faith, Faaaaith."*

Soon I was breathing, *"Faith, Faith, Faith."* I saw my breath as we stood in that circle, "Faith, Faith, Faith, Faith..." I was slowly starting to wash my brain and heart with *Faith.*

As my husband of deep faith and commitment cradled me in bed that night, I whispered, *"Faith, Faith, Faith. I have Faith..."* The next morning I awoke and wanted to understand what the Holy Spirit had revealed to my heart the night before. I found a verse in Hebrews 11 saying:

*"**Now faith is the assurance of things hoped for— divinely guaranteed—evidence for things not seen.**"*

I also found story after story of Jesus healing the sick, and He almost always followed up with, *"**Your faith has made you whole**"* or *"**Your faith has healed you.**"*

For me, faith was not an emotion; but a choice to believe God's Word. I believed God's promises in the Bible and what He revealed to me through the Holy Spirit. I knew that God loved me, that I would be healed and live to tell the story. That was my leap of faith. I chose to make that leap of faith on March 25, 2014. I believe with all my heart:

I am alive and thriving today all by the grace of God.

I am alive now to tell you the stories.

My faith is in God and His promises.

Doubt is the Opposite of Faith

During my past health challenges, I have learned to be careful who I discuss health decisions with. Well-meaning family and friends often don't understand when I tell them I am trusting God over the doctors. With the spot on my kidney, I did not want "doubt" and "fear" spoken over me. I wanted health, healing, and trust in God spoken over me.

With our health and healing, we need to turn to God more and less to man. Man often goes to medicine and fear. When we go to God and have faith in Him there is peace, healing, and relief from the anxieties of the world.

I once read in a devotional, "What I fear the most reveals where I trust God the least."

One day, I met a friendly African American woman downtown. We started chatting about health and healing. I told her the story about my back issue and spot on my kidney.

Jesus First Strategy:
Jesus says:
"Your *Faith* has made you whole."

She looked straight at me and her big brown eyes grew wide and she whispered clearly,

"If you doubt then there will be no healing." She was like an angel from heaven. I needed to trust in God's words:

"I will restore your health and heal your wounds... He healed them of all of their diseases... Your faith has made you whole." I also read in scripture that a *"double-minded man is unstable in all their ways,"* (James 1:8).

I remind myself that Jesus never turned anyone away who asked for healing. If any doubt creeps in I say,
"I rebuke you Satan, in the name of Jesus Christ who is my Lord and Savior and my Healer...Spirit of doubt and fear, leave now in the name of Jesus Christ! I am healed and whole!" (See Mark 16:17)

Repentance

Repentance precedes faith. It is in our best interest to live in a constant state of repentance and gratitude. My friend Karen asked me the other day, "What is repentance?"

After doing an online search, this is my favorite synopsis of repentance. "Repentance is a change of the mind, followed by a change of heart, followed by a change of action."

When we repent, we have a clean slate, then we can come boldly before the Lord that we may obtain mercy and grace.

When talking with a dear friend recently, she said that if we don't confess our sins first and repent, then God cannot hear our prayers. Our prayers may be **blocked** by that unrepentant sin, or unforgiveness.

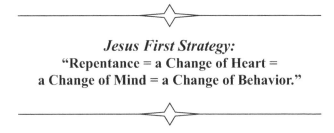

Jesus First Strategy:
"Repentance = a Change of Heart = a Change of Mind = a Change of Behavior."

"If I had not confessed the sin in my heart, the Lord would not have listened." (Psalm 66:18)

After healing a paralyzed man Jesus said to him, "See, you have been made well. Sin no more, lest a worse thing come upon you." Of course none of us are perfect, but we are called to make wise choices, seeking to "sin no more." Resist the devil and he will flee!

For me I often need to repent of succumbing to depression and anxiety, being slothful or being disobedient in doing what I know God is calling me to do; and also repenting of not being loving enough of "prickly" people in my life and of occasionally gorging on too many sweets and treats. I try to follow my repentance with gratitude for all the blessings in my life. It helps to declare new positive intentions for doing better in my areas of short comings.

James 5:16 says: *"Confess your faults to one another and pray for one another that **you may be healed**. The effective fervent prayer of a righteous man avails much,"* (James 5:16).

As our Pastor friend Rich Eddy preached, repentance is making a complete "U-TURN!"

I find great comfort in 1 John 1:9:

"If we confess our sins, He is faithful and just to forgive us our sins and to cleanse us from all unrighteousness."

It seems there is a direct correlation between our faith and His healing. Our faith activates the Holy Spirit and healing power. It's not that Jesus has to heal on demand, but He loves us enough to respond when we call out to Him with a humble, repentant heart. The Psalmist wrote, "He saves those who have a contrite spirit."

Stories of Faith: Then and Now

The word "faith" is in the New Testament 280 times, mostly in quotes by Jesus.

In the book of Matthew there is a remarkable story about a boy who is healed. A man came to Jesus... saying,

"Lord have mercy on my son, for he is an epileptic and suffers severely; he often falls into the fire and the water. I brought him to your disciples but they could not cure him."

Jesus continued, *"O faithless and perverse generation, how long shall I bear with you? Bring him here to Me. And Jesus rebuked the demon, and it came out of him; and the child was cured from that very hour."*

Then the disciples came to Jesus and said,

"Why could we not cast it out?" Jesus said,

"Because of your <u>unbelief</u>; for assuredly, I say to you, if you have faith as a mustard seed, you will say to this mountain, 'Move from here to there,' and it will move; and nothing will be impossible for you."

This story of the epileptic is a great example of why faith is so important. We must make the decision to believe in Jesus and His healing power and miracles. Our faith-filled prayers can activate God's powers for healing and miracles in our lives and the lives of others as well. God wants us to come to Him with child-like faith and ask.

One friend told me, "It's the belief that gets the miracle— Lay hands on your body and say, ***I believe!***" (Mark 16:18) Jesus says, 'you will do these things and even greater.' (John 14:12)

Remember the story about the paralyzed man whose friends lowered him down the hole in the roof anticipating Jesus would heal their friend? And of course, Jesus healed him. **Faith is an act.** In the Bible James reminds us that,

"Faith without works is dead."

It is not referring to physical *work* in this verse, but rather, 'do our life choices reflect our faith'? Do we believe in Jesus' healing power and yet give all control to the medical community? How is our faith really being demonstrated?

Lessons on faith and trust can come from unexpected places. A Sister in faith has a large Labrador retriever named Bear. This faithful dog has a large water bowl located in the corner of the kitchen. Whenever it is empty Bear will not bark or paw at the water bowl. Instead, he will lie down quietly and wait. Sometimes he has to wait awhile, but Bear has learned to trust his owner will eventually walk in the room, see him there and provide what he needs. His simple faith reminds us to place more trust in God. Sometimes we just need a lot of patience.

God is faithful to keep His promises to all who believe and come to Him through Jesus. This is the BEST news ever!

I recently heard a story about a tightrope walker who crossed over the Niagara Falls. Before he crosses on a tightrope, he asks the crowd:

"How many of you think I can cross Niagara Falls on a tightrope with a plate in my hand?" They all raise their hand and cheer. And he does it. Next, he asks,

"How many here believe I can cross Niagara Falls with this wheelbarrow?" And they all raise their hands eagerly.

Then the tightrope walker does that too. His next question is, "How many of you believe I can cross the falls with a *person* in the wheelbarrow?"

And they all raise their hands once again.

Finally, he asks, "Who is willing to go in the wheelbarrow while I cross Niagara Falls?"

And not one hand goes up...

I wonder if sometimes our lack of faith is similar. Is our faith like Peter in the Bible, who when he had his eyes on Jesus was able to walk on water, then lost his focus and started to sink. May we keep our eyes upon Jesus...

The Apostle Paul, became a "Jesus Follower" after being struck blind in the desert and then healed and restored by the Lord. Later, Paul followed Jesus' instruction to 'fast and heal' others in the name of the Lord. (Acts 13:3)

One day, Paul observed that a crippled man had "faith to be healed." Paul said with a loud voice, "Stand up straight on your feet!" And the man leaped and walked. (Acts 14:9-10)

The common thread between all the stories of Jesus' healings in the Bible is *faith*. We can grab onto that same faith, having confidence in Jesus, His healing power, and His desire for wholeness and restoration.

Jesus First Strategy:
"All things are possible to him who believes."
Mark 9:23

Jesus said He came to give us 'abundant life' and God said He wants to give us 'hope and a future'.

One faithful friend says: "We say we trust God for healing on Sunday and then run to the doctors and pharmacies on Monday." Faith takes God at His Word and trusts God completely, stepping out and boldly believing the things He has promised.

> **"Faith is not believing that God can,**
> **it's knowing that He will..."**

My Prayer: *"Dear God, thank You for healing me from cancers, bleeding fibroids, depression, anxiety, sloth, eating issues, and much more. I repent of my slip-ups and I ask that You help me do better. I commit to turning from my sins. I have faith that You will keep me healthy, whole, and give me peace. Please give me more faith! Thank You, Lord!"*
Love Your Daughter, Liz

Your Prayer and Reflection: What specific things can you do to increase your faith?

_____

_____

_____

God's Temple
Bought at a Price

"Do you not know that your bodies are temples of the Holy Spirit,... you are not your own? You are bought at a price. Therefore honor God with your bodies."
— 1 Corinthians 6:19-20

Our body is merely a 'vehicle' that has been given to us by God.

If a friend loaned you a brand-new car would you treat it with the utmost care? Would you drive it beyond its limit? Would you bang it around? Would you pour sugar, coca cola, or vodka into the gas tank?

When we don't take good care of this wonderful vehicle called the body, a temple of God, in some sense we are disrespecting God and His great gift to us.

A wise counselor once mentioned, "We are all responsible for our own backyard as adults."

I asked her what she meant by that, and she continued,

"We are responsible for our feelings, our choices, our emotions, and our decisions. We can decide what we think, we can decide what we eat and we can make decisions on how we take care of our temples spiritually and physically."

I asked her about friends and families' backyards, and she said,

"We are not responsible for anyone else's backyard but our own."

The following is a take home list of the responsibilities in our "own backyard."

My Backyard List:

- **My spiritual life~ how much time and energy I focus on prayer, praise and studying God's Word.**
- **My feelings and how I react to things.**
- **My thoughts and what I focus on.**
- **My actions and choices and the words that come out of my mouth (remembering, life and death are in the power of the tongue). Do my words and actions match?**
- **My attitudes – I can choose to see the cup as half full or half empty. I can choose joy!**
- **How I handle my spouse, family and friend relationships. Do I pray with my spouse?**

- The boundaries in my backyard. Whether I build walls or fences. I can choose who I spend time with and who I listen to; including TV, media, books, and music.
- The condition of my heart. Have I repented and accepted God's forgiveness for my sins and have I forgiven others? If there are "toxic people", I can forgive them without necessarily allowing them back into my backyard; yet letting go of bitterness.
- The food I buy at the store for me and my family.
- The food I prepare and eat.
- The drinks that I choose to consume.
- My literal "backyard", body and home. What cleaning products, fertilizers, and personal body products do I choose to use?
- The medicines and supplements I take.
- My exercise routine.
- The way I choose to spend my money.
- How much time I rest and relax.
- The way I spend my time.

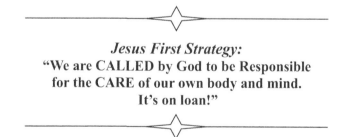

Jesus First Strategy:
"We are CALLED by God to be Responsible
for the CARE of our own body and mind.
It's on loan!"

From the "backyard list" above, I have highlighted two of my favorites. One is on *"Joy"* and the other is on *"Rest"*.

Joy

The classic movie, *Pollyanna,* reminds us of how important it is to choose joy and gladness. Pollyanna is a ten-year-old girl who helps teach a town to choose gladness over bitterness. She taught her friends "the glad game" where she challenges them to take a negative situation and find the good instead. Then later in the movie she is talking with the pastor of the town and encourages him with these words:

"My father discovered the 'Glad' passages, you know, the happy ones like 'shout for joy' or 'be glad in the Lord'. There are **800 Happy Texts**...Daddy said if God took the trouble to tell us 800 times to be glad and rejoice, He must have wanted us to do it!"

In my own life it is a constant struggle. After my breast cancer diagnosis in 2014, I fell prey to great anxiety. Once when I met with my Christian counselor, Sue, for guidance this is what she told me:

"You have a choice, Elizabeth, to choose peace or choose fear during this breast cancer journey."

I told her I wanted to choose peace but the fearful, anxious thoughts kept creeping into my mind. I asked Sue, "How do I choose peace?"

She said, "Just do it! It's like that commercial, just do it. Just choose peace. Refuse to entertain the lies of satan. Speak the word of God. Say, 'Jesus Christ is my Lord and Savior, I stand on the word of God.' Say it out loud! The enemy can't stand in the same room with Jesus, he will flee."

Rest

*Ahhh, **rest**.* It seems to always be at the bottom of the list; yet we long for it and we need it. One time, to advertise a vacation property Eric and I managed, we used a message from Jesus, for weary visitors: *"Come to Me, all who labor and are heavy laden, and I will give you rest."* (Matthew 11:28) The place was booked.

The Lord reminds us to take some quiet time with Him. The twenty-third Psalm is one of my favorites. One time at a somber Church service on Ash Wednesday before Easter, the Pastor asked those who knew Psalms 23 by heart, to recite it together. It surprised me as the words rolled off my tongue: *"He makes me to lie down in green pastures. He leads me besides the still waters. He restores my soul..."* This verse gives us all permission to take time and rest...in fact "He makes me to lie down..." It sounds like a command for our own good; like resting on the Sabbath, on Sundays.

When we **rest** our body has a chance to heal, mend and repair itself. With our busy schedules we need to be vigilant to carve out times to rest.

In our society today many of us do not get enough sleep at night. Studies have shown that getting enough sleep helps ward off disease, including cancer. I'm not saying this to scare you because I know we all probably lack enough sleep. However, we do need to make sleep a priority. Studies have also shown that a twenty-minute nap in the afternoon can be beneficial too.

As we age our bodies have less melatonin production for sleep. So my husband and I take a one milligram (smallest dose) of natural melatonin and one probiotic capsule (for the digestion) every night before bed. Other sleep pointers are:

- Have a dark, quiet, cool bedroom to sleep in.
- Keep the bedroom reserved for sleep and romance.
- Oversleeping can cause problems too. Studies show that people who sleep too much have higher depression, obesity and diabetes.
- Seven to nine hours is recommended, with 8 hours a night as a "sweet spot."
- Lavender oil on the skin or in a diffuser helps induce a feeling of peace, calm, and sleep. Try rubbing a little lavender oil mixed with coconut oil above your top lip and on the back of your neck before bed.
- Remember to pray with your spouse, read scripture and maybe listen to a Christian song before bed. Did you know that couples that pray together daily have a 99% *staying married rate*, according to a Gallup Poll?

My Prayer: *"Dear God, thank You for this miraculous self-healing body You gave me. Forgive me for sometimes abusing it with food, negative thoughts, and not enough rest and exercise. Starting today I will do better. Help me to stick with it, as my continued habits define my life. I want to please You God with my body. Thank You for helping me with all of this."*

Love, Your Grateful Daughter, Liz

Your Prayer and Reflection: What can you do to better take care of your body?

_____

_____

_____

"Proclaiming the good works of the Lord!"

Why Live?

"I shall not die, but live, and declare the works of the Lord."— Psalm 118:17

The healing service was scheduled for 4:00pm for Grace. I had never met Grace, but her mother had asked if my husband and I would be willing to sing some songs and encourage her, as she had just had a cancerous tumor removed from her brain. The doctors had told her that they got 99% of the tumor out, but that it was still an aggressive cancer and she likely had 15 months to live.

As Eric and I prepared music and were praying about the healing service; we planned a communion, anointing with oil, healing songs, a time of repentance, and prayers.

Grace arrived joining in the faithful group that was there to support her. She wore a fleece hat and warm coat, giving me a big hug with smiles, and yet I saw some fear in her eyes.

Healing Service and Prayer

We opened the healing service with some sharing from Grace. She requested prayer and music. I asked if I might pray for her first. The Holy Spirit spoke through me with the following (lengthy!) prayer:

"Dear Lord, we thank you and praise You, we love You! We thank you for Grace. We are believing and receiving that any remaining disease is being removed completely and that Grace is healed. We thank You for all of Your Bible Promises. You say, 'I will restore your health and heal your wounds' and 'by Your stripes we are healed'.

Lord, in the book of James you say, 'confess your faults to one another and pray for one another that ye may be healed!' We confess now our sins. We repent. We gratefully receive your forgiveness.

And God, we remember the story of the woman with the issue of bleeding for twelve years, and the fact that she went to many physicians and grew not better but worse. And she spent all of her money. And then she thought to herself, if only I can touch the hem of Jesus' robe, I know I will be healed – And she pushed through the crowd and touched His robe and immediately her flow of blood dried up!

Then Jesus turned around and said, 'Daughter your faith has made you whole, go in peace and be healed of your affliction.' And Lord we remember that no one in the Bible who came to Jesus for healing was turned away! And You healed them of all diseases, not just some, but all.

You say 'I am the Lord who heals you'. And you say I am the same yesterday, today, and tomorrow. And You say that as

Your disciples we will do these things and even greater! We are your disciples now.

You delivered me from 3 cancers, I am so grateful—I believe You will do the same healing for Grace. I praise You Lord! You say to come boldly before the throne of God and make our requests. Here we are Lord!

You say I am the Alpha and Omega, the beginning and end. And over and over Jesus said, 'your faith has made you whole'. Lord, we are gathered here as Grace's friends today and are lowering her down through the roof just like the story in the Bible.

And so now we do come boldly before the throne, asking for healing for our dear friend Grace.

We pray that Grace is whole and can go in peace and be free of all disease. Please embolden her faith!

And Lord, You say, if any of you need wisdom to ask, and You will give it liberally. So we ask for wisdom on her next steps with the doctors and treatments, always remembering that You are our Great Physician.

Please guide Grace with Your eye. Comfort her. Help her to sleep at night. Take away her anxiety. You say, 'cast your burdens upon Me and I will sustain you...'

We thank You and praise You and we love You, and we go forth in peace and joy in anticipation that Grace will have a huge testimony to share of Your great healing and Your great love. *In Jesus name, Amen.*" My prayer was *finally* finished.

Healing Songs and Communion

After our prayers, we sang several Worshipful Hymns, including a song Eric and I had recently written called,

The Healing Song~ Keeper of my Soul. The lyrics are at the end of this book. Then we had a gluten free semi-Keto communion.

We finished up the Healing Service with Grace's Dad, who is a retired minister, anointing us all with oil. I was so thankful as my Mom arrived toward the end of the service because she is battling a blood disease. A powerful healing scripture was read while we specifically anointed and prayed over Grace and my Mom:

> *"Is anyone among you sick? Let him call for the elders of the Church, and let them pray over him, anointing him with oil in the name of the Lord. And the prayer of faith will save the sick and the Lord will raise him up. Confess your sins to one another and pray for one another that you may be healed. The effective, fervent prayer of a righteous man avails much"* (James 5:14-16).

We ended the service with big hugs and vowed to stay in touch. I gave Grace a copy of my testimonial book, *Floored and Delivered*, and I gave her a one-inch little white Bible, that has one verse from each book in the Bible.

Grace's Faith

Several days later, Grace and I chatted on the phone. She expressed her great gratitude for the healing service; we had an unspoken common bond.

She said, "Oh, Elizabeth I have a miracle story to share with you. A few nights ago, I lay awake with my usual insomnia, and fear set in. I asked God to help me. Then I reached over on my nightstand and picked up the tiny Bible you gave me, and I opened it up. Guess what the verse was on that page? It was from John. It said:

'I live that ye may live also' Can you believe that!?"

We were both blown away by God's amazing love and confirmation.

We prayed together on the phone thanking God for that wonderful encouragement and confirmation. And my prayer for Grace is that she will believe that special verse with all her heart!

Several months after the Healing Service with Grace, I sent her a text of encouragement that said:

'I shall not die, but live,
   and declare the works
   of the LORD'

Right afterward, Grace returned a text message saying:

'Oh my goodness Elizabeth—
Just a few days ago,
I asked God for a confirmation.
Randomly, I turned to one page
in the Bible. It was THIS same verse!
The same scripture you sent continued:
The LORD hath chastened me sore; but he hath
not given me over unto death—Psalms 118.
I knew this was direct from God.
I thought of you writing 'Liz Lives.'
This is no coincidence!
It is God's truth active in our lives.
Sending you a heartful of love. *Grace*'

My last text message that night to Grace was:

'Amen! Praise The Lord for these confirmations,

I believe that *you* will live and not die
and you will proclaim the good news of the Lord!
Let's make that our reason to live!'

Grace and I have continued texting and praying together and the most recent text she sent to me reads:

'Hey Elizabeth, if you want to add this following info (to your book), feel free... I have chosen to reject "standard of care" and instead to pursue a Naturopathic healing path along with prayer – as a step of faith and trust in God's healing power through Jesus Christ!!"

Why Live?

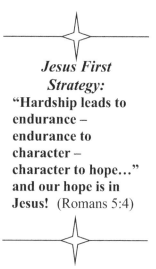

Jesus First Strategy:
"Hardship leads to endurance –
endurance to character –
character to hope..."
and our hope is in Jesus! (Romans 5:4)

We each need to wrestle within our heart with the question;

"Why do I want to live?"

Studies show that when we have a *reason to live* that our odds are a lot better for surviving dreaded diseases, and living longer. And once we decide why we want to live, we need to decide how to live.

When I was going through my trial of breast cancer, one of my friends spoke powerful words over me.

"Elizabeth you are afflicted, but not beat down." She continued, "I will restore your health and heal your wounds, says the Lord, according to Jeremiah 30:17." The icing on the cake was when she said to me, "Think of the amazing testimony you will have to share, once you have come through and beat this cancer."

She was right. God healed me and I have a testimony to share. In fact, my husband Eric and I have been blessed as "Musical Missionaries" to share our testimonies and original songs at churches, concerts and women's events. I now share my life-story book *Floored and Delivered: A Tell-All Testimony of God's Love, Healing and Forgiveness.* God has revealed this new purpose in my life to share the Good News through writing, speaking and singing. The Psalms say: "I will not die, but live and declare what God has done in my life!"

My Prayer: *"Thank You God for bearing with me. Help me to fill my mind with Your life-giving promises. Today I choose joy. Today I choose life. Today I choose to eat healthy. By Your grace today I live with a purpose to share that joy and the Good News of Jesus with others. I love You!"*
Love Your Daughter, Liz

Your Prayer and Reflection: What is your purpose in life? Why do you want to live?

_____

_____

_____

41

My People Perish

My people perish for lack of knowledge…"
—Hosea 4:6

*M*y first scare with cancer was in the summer of 2002, as my seventeen-year first marriage was grinding to an end.

It all started when I noticed a dark red substance in the toilet. I tried to explain it away for months by telling myself, *"Oh I ate beets last night"* or *"I had strawberry jam;"* anything could have caused the dark red stains. At forty-one years old, it was hard to imagine it might be serious. Then a stool test came back showing blood. Afterward, an urgent call came in from the gastro doctor:

"Elizabeth—you need to schedule a colonoscopy immediately." While waiting, I ruminated on the "C word…"

A week later, I gulped down the horrible tasting gallon of saline water. My intestines were cleared out after running to the bathroom nearly a dozen times during the night.

Doctor Goldberg asked if I wanted to be semi-conscious during the colonoscopy, and I said "Sure." I felt light headed and a bit dizzy as the IV meds kicked in. I gazed at the TV screen monitor as the snake-like probe was going through my colon and intestines.

All was going well until Dr. Goldberg said, "I need some help here Sandy," in a stern voice, and "I need to cut this out."

Even in my semi-conscious state, my heart sank. I saw on the screen a round, ugly, red- veined, marble-sized growth.

Is this what a demon looks like? I wondered.

It looked menacing. "Snip" and it was gone.

A few days later I got the results from the biopsy from the colonoscopy, and sure enough it was evil. It was a cancerous, malignant polyp. The grape sized polyp was removed during the colonoscopy; however, I would need to schedule a major surgery to remove twelve inches of my lower intestine to make sure it was all out. The surgeon was concerned that the cancer may have spread beyond the colon wall.

The surgery was major. After the several hour procedure was complete, I lay in the hospital bed and looked down at a six-inch incision that started as a question mark around my belly button. I reflected on my life; my young daughters, my faith, and ultimately what landed me in the hospital with colon cancer. My quest for Truth was reignited.

The surgery removed the diseased cells. No Chemo. No Radiation. But I did NOT want to end up in the hospital again...little did I know, there would be 2 more episodes with this same dreaded disease.

My research path began. What I have found, I reveal in the following chapters of this book. My colon cancer was likely caused by years of alcohol consumption, years of constipation, major stress and anxiety, and a diet high in carbs and sugar. We all can be so stubborn about researching things, and even more stubborn about accepting the truths and most stubborn about making change in our life.

"My people perish" is a compelling thought. We all know the saying, "Knowledge is Power". And James 1:5 tells us that *if you ask God for wisdom, He will give it generously.* In this book, I am sharing with you proven strategies, raw data, and examples of how to get and stay healthy, both spiritually and physically. I encourage you to do your own research, and to *own* and apply the information. Ephesians 5 says to 'EXPOSE evil'. And Jesus says, "The Truth shall set you free!"

Learn from Others

Why do we often push away new information even when there is valid research and scientific data to back it up? Remember when we thought cigarettes were healthy and doctors came on "Camel" commercials saying: *"More doctors smoke Camel cigarettes than any other brand?"* but research showed smoking causes cancer. Now cancer is everyone's concern. If you flip a coin, there is now a one in two chance—or 50%—that the cancer coin will land heads up.

According to the Mayo Clinic, half of all people may get cancer in their lifetime. Studies show everyone has a few stray cancer cells lurking in their bodies. We can learn tips from others on staying healthy. By investing in our health now, we can avoid hospitals later.

Not only are cancer rates skyrocketing, but so is diabetes.

My dear friend was extremely overweight. Diabetes, wheelchairs, needles and foot surgeries from the diabetes were a constant part of her life.

I pleaded with her one day, "Ana, I love you so much. You are a dear sister in Christ. I am concerned for your health. You are a mighty woman of God—an important part of His army."

I looked her in the eyes and continued in a soft voice, "I have a great book on health and food from God's perspective that I would like to give you if you're interested."

She smiled and said thank you, and indicated, "I'll think about it." Seven years passed, and it was never mentioned again until her brother lost both legs at the knee due to diabetes. Ana has now lost several pounds and decided to make lifestyle changes.

Jesus First Strategy: "Sometimes we are so stubborn...we will go to our graves with our ears plugged and our eyes shut!"

I suppose sometimes we are ready for knowledge and change when we are up against the wall. Sometimes we are so stubborn, we go to our graves with our ears plugged and eyes shut. We hear the truth but we would rather perish in our comfy habits rather than make changes for the better.

My husband Eric sometimes jests, "What's the difference between '*Ignorance* and *Apathy*?" Answer: "I don't know and I don't care..."

I know this concept well. It took me three cancers before I was willing to make big changes in my life.

My colon cancer came first, followed by melanoma, and finally breast cancer; double mastectomy. God addresses this sin nature in the book of Jeremiah: "***Hear this, you foolish and senseless people, who have eyes but do not see, who have ears but do not hear.***" (Jeremiah 5:21)

One Sunday, Eric and I shared some of our original music and testimony at a church revival in the Carolinas. A young seminary student, from the Baptist Theological Seminary in Dallas, shared an amazing message that day. It had been a long time since we heard such spirit filled teaching. Pastor Duncan began the sermon with humility:

"I am a man of unclean lips." His message implored believers to tell the *Gospel Truth*. "Don't be surprised when people don't listen. Tell them anyway." God says, His Word will not return void. Duncan continued with this powerful scripture:

> "And He said, 'Go, and tell this people:
> Keep on hearing, but do not understand;
> Keep on seeing, but do not perceive.
> Make the heart of this people dull,
> And their ears heavy, and shut their eyes;
> Lest they see with their eyes and hear with their ears,
> And understand with their heart,
> And return and be healed.'" - Isaiah 6

Isaiah does not give a popular message.

Often, we behave like an ostrich with its *head in the sand* rather than following the message God has for us.

Is Ignorance Bliss? I don't think so. After walking the hospital hallways in a thin blue gown holding an IV pole so many times, I implore you dear friends, seek knowledge and make the changes. This message is shared out of love.

Online searches usually list pharmaceutical medicines before the natural remedies. The drug companies often pay companies like Google to promote their drugs. Explore the options for a more unbiased private search. Seek truth and God's natural remedies always. You never know what you may find...

One day while researching online, I discovered a potential remedy for some cancers! An Italian Oncologist declared: "**Cancer is a *Fungus*** called *Candida (albicans)* and it can be treated using Sodium Bicarbonate *(Baking Soda)*." The idea is to alkalize the body, eliminate Candida, shrink tumors and stop metastases. He says simply, "It's the natural cancer cure!"

Letter to my Doctor

I encourage anyone diagnosed with cancer to write a letter similar to the one below written to my breast cancer doctor. We are called to take responsibility for our own health.

"Dear Medical Doctors,

This letter is to notify you that I take full responsibility for my health and decisions regarding my health care. I appreciate your recommendations and testing. My husband and I will ***prayerfully consider*** and **research** all of our options and let you know what medical plan we determine going forward. You are hereby released of any and all liability." Sincerely, *Elizabeth Soldahl*

Scripture says;

"The fear of the Lord is the beginning of wisdom,"

I personally have a healthy fear of the Lord after facing three cancers; I know He has sovereign power. Yet, our Heavenly Father designed us to live long in health and abundance! He designed our bodies to heal naturally.

If we desire wisdom, we are to ask God and He will give it liberally. How does one find wisdom? We find wisdom in God's Word, the Holy Bible. That is our Go-To. Eric says BIBLE stands for 'Basic Instructions Before Leaving Earth'!

My Prayer: *"Dear God, thank You for revealing so much information to me and directing me to scripture regarding health and healing. Forgive me for not getting this book out sooner. Please help me to quickly get this message out to help others on their healing journey. Thank You for Your physical healing and forgiveness of my sins."*

Love Your Daughter, Liz

Your Prayer and Reflection: What can you do to shift your heart to see and hear the truth? What is keeping you from hearing the truth and acting on it?

_____

_____

_____

Speak it Forth

"For as he thinketh in his heart, so is he."
—Proverbs 23:7

*A*manda was a woman of great faith and she loved the Lord; however, she was **deathly** afraid of getting sick.

"Disease runs in my family," Amanda said sadly, one day.

In fact many people in her life had died of cancer. The devil had gotten a foothold on her mind and caused her to have this worry. She told many people of her fear of cancer. She was a *warrior and a worrier* at the same time. Eventually, Amanda did get sick. Amanda died from cancer and chemo.

Negative thinking is of the devil, and it often leads to depression and possible disease. I wonder if Amanda knew the power of praying God's promises back to Him? Could her outcome have been different if she spoke forth life instead of death?

"Sometimes it seems we want to *cover our bases*, by preparing for the worst," one friend mentioned later.

But just because cancer *runs in the family*, doesn't mean we are doomed. Jesus has given us the authority to break Generational Curses in His Name.

We can repent and ask God to forgive us of negative, anxious thinking and to, 'take all our thoughts captive to Jesus.' When we dwell on negative thoughts it is poisoning from within. It could even lead to disease. When we speak negatively, it cements those thoughts.

God is listening, other people are listening, our bodies are listening, and the devil, who is the "prince of the air," may be listening when we speak. It is important to note that the devil is NOT omniscient, or all-knowing like God. The devil can't read our minds or know our thoughts, however, if we say something, he or his demons lurking around may seize upon it to influence us. Eric and I pray daily asking God to bind up Satan and his demons from our home and family. We pray to have God place His angels of protection around us.

I've struggled off and on with the spirit of infirmity and dread of disease ever since my cancer episodes.

When I received my breast cancer diagnosis in 2014 my friend sent me a text, she said,

"Elizabeth don't allow depression to sink in. Remember, singing is 'speaking forth' with a melody and is powerful and effective. It's hard to be depressed or negative when you are singing. So, sing in the shower, sing in the kitchen, just sing."

Sometimes I pray and mediate on a Bible verse. It all starts with trust: *"Trust in the Lord with all your heart, and lean not on your own understanding; in all your ways acknowledge Him and He shall direct your paths...**it will be health to your flesh and strength to your bones**."* (Proverbs 3:6-8)

Proclaim Deliverance

Mr. Knox is a Deliverance Healing Minister. God has delivered me from several strongholds in my life with the help of this elder man of God. One day I called him in a bit of a panic as I feared another illness in my life. He spoke with great authority, in the name of Jesus Christ:

Jesus First Strategy: **Proclaim: "I will live a Long and Healthy Life until the Day the Lord takes me Home!"**

"We cast the spirit of infirmity, cancer and fear off of Elizabeth and I pray right now in the name of Jesus Christ of Nazareth, that Elizabeth will live a long healthy life until the day the Lord takes her home to heaven!"

Whenever I start to feel fear again, I remember that prayer, and pray it to the Lord. *Did you know that God never says we need to die of disease?* We must die someday, but disease and cancer were not in God's plan. Old age and natural causes, yes; Disease, no.

Here is another powerful Deliverance Prayer that I pray:

"Dear God, forgive my sin of not trusting You with my health; I repent. I dedicate my mind and body to You. In the name of Jesus, I command every demon to leave now; including the *Spirits of Cancer, Mistrust, Infirmity* (or_____ *insert whatever the Holy Spirit reveals*). *Let Your healing flow!* Thank you, Lord! In Jesus' name, Amen (refer to Mark 16:17)

The "C" Word

I try to avoid the word *cancer*. I try to refer to it as the "C word" or "past disease" because I don't want my body to even hear that word. I want to speak forth positive healing words not negative disease words. There are studies that show that living, growing plants that have been talked to sweetly grow healthy and strong and green; and plants that are yelled at or talked to in negative ways don't thrive in the same manner. Similar concepts apply to children. And even scientific research backs it up:

*A **New research project from Duke University reveals that our thoughts may actually change our DNA. Wow!***

Yellow Sticky Notes

While going through my breast cancer ordeal, I met with my Christian counselor and told her all my fears. One day I felt confident and strong of my faith and the next I was a wreck. The highs and lows were too much to handle, I explained to her.

Thankfully, my counselor was full of wisdom. Sue helped me correct some of my wrong thinking about my breast cancer.

Counselor Sue, reminded me that,

"With God all things are possible."

My counseling session ended that day with a prayer and a big hug, and as I stepped out of her office, I felt renewed. She encouraged me to look up in my Bible Ephesians 6:11-12.

When I got home, this is what I read:

*"Put on the whole armor of God that you may be
able to stand against the wiles of the devil.
For we do not wrestle against flesh and blood,
but against principalities, against powers,
and against rulers of the darkness of this age."*

The day after my counseling session I posted yellow sticky notes throughout our home and started speaking forth expectations of healing. I recited Gods promises from the Bible out loud. These are what my scripture sticky notes read:

- *"Your faith has made you well."*
- *"Resist the devil and he will flee!"*
- *"God forgives my sins and heals my diseases!"*
- *"By His stripes I am healed."*
- *"I will restore your health and heal your wounds, says the Lord."*
- *"Faith is the assurance of things hoped for – the evidence of things not seen."*
- *"A thousand may fall at my side, and ten thousand at my right hand but it shall not come near me."*
- *"He who began a good work in me will carry it on to completion until the day of Christ Jesus!"*

Not long ago, I suffered from a two-week bladder infection. At church, I asked the elders to anoint me with oil, as according to James 5:14, *"Is any sick among you? Let him call for the elders of the church; and let them pray over him, anointing him with oil in the name of the Lord."* And then:

"The prayer of faith shall save the sick..."

When I returned home after the prayers at church, I spoke out loud: *"In the name of Jesus, I RESIST YOU SATAN, GET OUT OF MY **MIND** AND BODY! I BELONG TO JESUS; I AM A CHILD OF GOD! – By the stripes of Jesus I am healed."*

The Bible implores us to use the word of God to speak in response to the enemy. We can speak forth life in abundance: *"Let the weak say I am strong."* We can *"Call those things that are not, as though they are."* (Romans 4:17) With faith, we are called to proclaim results instead of problems!

My Prayer: *"Holy spirit flush my system and purify my blood with the healing blood of Jesus. I believe and receive your healing. Forgive me for doubting. Take away my spirit of infirmity or fear. I declare that I will live a long and healthy life until the day You take me home. I will believe and speak forth your amazing promises! Thank you Lord!
In Jesus Name, Amen."*

Your Daughter, Liz

Your Prayer and Reflection: What Bible Promises and Prayers can you *'**speak forth**'*? How can you combat the enemy?

_____

_____

_____

God's Word

"Man shall not live by bread alone, but by every word that proceeds from the mouth of God."—Matthew 4:4 & Luke 4:4

"Your wife is dying—not from cancer but from chemo," a compassionate nurse told Bonnie's husband at the cancer center.

Bonnie was diagnosed in 2015 with stage 3 breast cancer. She had extensive chemo, radiation, and a lumpectomy. At her rock bottom she prayed to God for help and He directed her to Psalm 91:

"A thousand may fall at your side and ten thousand at your right hand but it shall not come near you...With long life I will satisfy him, and show him My salvation."

There was a short remission, but in 2017 cancer resurfaced in her cervix. Once again, she started chemo and radiation both inside and out. Bonnie became sicker and sicker saying, "Satan has an attack on me with a death wish." This wasn't far from the truth.

In her weakest moment, Bonnie opened her Bible once again, believing the promises in Romans 8:28:

"And we know that all things work together for good to those who love God, to those who are the called according to His purpose."

The weekend before her next scheduled chemo therapy and radiation, she received phone calls from two different prayer warrior friends with warnings.

One friend said, "I feel death coming over you, and I feel you need to stop those treatments."

Soon after, Bonnie lay in bed at the hospital and she heard someone whisper in her ear "I love you!" There was no one in the room! A sweet peace came over Bonnie and it was then that she knew God had answered her healing prayer and fulfilled His promises from Romans and the Psalms.

In that moment Bonnie knew she was healed by God! Against the advice of her physicians she stopped all chemo and radiation treatments. She now proclaims to others, "God healed me of my deadly disease." To this day, Bonnie is healthy and whole (although she does suffer from the long-term effects of radiation and chemotherapy).

Isaiah 55:11 says, "God's Word <u>does not</u> return void." Pray God's 'promises' back to Him and believe that He will hold to His word. Let's *Ingest the Word*—let's gobble *it up!*

"If my word abides in you, you will ask what you desire and it shall be done for you. (John 15:7)

Jesus' Words

At the start of His ministry, Jesus was alone for forty days and nights in the barren desert. He ate nothing at all and then the devil tempted Him.

Satan came to Jesus and said to Him: *"If Thou are the Son of God, command that these stones turn into loaves of bread."*

But the Lord answered him at once: *"It is written in God's Word, 'Man shall not live on bread alone, but on every word that proceeds from the mouth of God.'"*

Three times the devil had tempted Jesus and each time Jesus responded by using scripture—the Word of God. The devil had to flee upon hearing God's word.

Since Jesus had prayed and fasted for forty days He was spiritually fit for the battle.

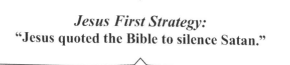

Jesus First Strategy:
"Jesus quoted the Bible to silence Satan."

The Bible is the inspired Word of God. Through His Word He reveals the salvation plan through His Son, Jesus who is God in flesh. His Word is a lamp unto our path.

God's Word is God's Food. His Word sustains us. God's Word, or the Bible, is referred to as the Bread of Life. I like how a friend referred to the Bible in this way:

"God says it. I believe it. That settles it!"

I would like to share some other *Jesus First Strategy* Bible Verses:

- *"My word will never pass away,"* (Mark 13:31).
- *"My daughter, your faith has made you well, go in peace and be healed of your affliction,"* (Mark 5:34).
- *"Don't be afraid, only believe,"* (Mark 5:36).
- *"I know the plans I have for you says the Lord, plans of hope and a future,"* (Jeremiah 29:11).

- Jesus said, *"I came to give you life in abundance,"* (John 10:10).
- *"Confess your sins to one another, and pray for one another, that you may be healed. The effective fervent prayer of a righteous man avails much,"* (James 5:16).
- *"Life and death is in the power of the tongue,"* (Proverbs 18:21).
- *"For the Word of God is living and powerful,"* (Hebrews 4:12).
- *"I can do all things through Christ who strengthens me,"* (Philippians 4:13).
- *"Everyone who calls on the name of the Lord will be saved,"* (Acts 2:21).
- Jesus said, *"I am the way the truth and the life, no one comes to the father except through Me,"* (John 14:6).
- *"Resist the devil and he will flee from you,"* (James 4:7).

Scripture refers to the Word of God as a Sword. It is something to be wielded as a *First Strategy* to deal with the enemy and every trial, including health trials.

"And take the helmet of salvation and the sword of the spirit, which is the Word of God," (Ephesians 6:17).

The Bible, God's Word, has *all* of the answers. If you have any issues in life you can look it up in the concordance (index) of your Bible or do an online search to find where and how God addresses the issue. Look to His Word for answers. John 17:17 says: *"God's Word is truth."*

God's Word and Healing a Broken Heart

It was on a quiet, walk in the forest with my dear young friend that the miracle occurred. As we sat by a small water cascade, she opened her heart to me and her voice trembled:

"Elizabeth, I had an abortion last year." Her body started to shake as her eyes filled with tears. "I am so sad about it. I killed my baby...and maybe I won't be able to have another." She sobbed uncontrollably. "It was a baby girl." Tears rushed liked the little waterfall beside us.

I held her close, then looked into her huge, doe-like eyes, "Oh sweetie, I am soo sorry..."

She told me of the blood, the pain, and the delivery of her dead baby in her bathroom after taking the chemical abortion pills. She said, "How can I ever forgive myself?"

I held her hands and told her how Jesus loved her and died on the cross for our sins according to His Word in John 3:16. I shared with her about my stillborn baby Stephanie, and how I was forgiven and healed by God, and that I had assurance that I would see her in Heaven one day. I asked her, "Would you like forgiveness, the promise of Heaven too?"

She said, "yes" in a soft voice.

"Would you like to say a prayer of forgiveness and salvation with me?"

"Yes." She whispered and smiled.

"Dear God," she repeated my words. "Thank you for loving me enough to send Jesus to die for me. I know I am a sinner and I repent. Please forgive me for everything I've done. I am so sorry. I accept your forgiveness today, and accept Jesus as the Lord and leader of my life. Amen."

When I opened my eyes, I saw the most beautiful glowing child of God in front of me smiling with glimmering eyes.

"Did He really do that for me?"

"Yes," I said, "and you have just made the *most* important decision of your life."

Then we took off our shoes and walked into the water and splashed our faces with the chilly winter waterfall. I gave her a big hug and told her she was *born anew*. We put our shoes back on and went home for a bowl of warm keto chicken vegetable soup.

The Ultimate Healing:

My dear reader friend, if you haven't accepted Jesus as your Lord and Savior, I urge you to do it now. No matter what you have done in the past, God forgives those who turn to Him asking for forgiveness. Here are the ABC's of how to do it. Open your heart and pray the following in your own words:

A. <u>Admit</u> to God that you are a sinner. Be sorry for past sins and commit to turning away from them.

B. <u>Believe</u> that God loves you so much that He sent His Son, Jesus, to die on the cross to pay the penalty for sin.

C. <u>Confess</u> faith in Jesus Christ as your Savior and Lord. Then make Him the Lord and leader of your life.

If you prayed that prayer and meant it, you truly made the most important decision in your whole life. This is the **ultimate healing**. Part of this transformed life includes reading the Bible and praying daily, telling others of your decision, and hanging around with other true believers. Beware, there are a lot of false teachers and false churches and false Christians in the world today. Choose carefully.

Remember God's Word, in 1 Corinthians emphasizes being *"equally yoked,"* This means in marriage or any close relationship, that both people should be Jesus Followers.

God's Promises: *"For God so loved the world that he sent His only begotten Son that whosoever believeth in Him shall not perish but have everlasting life."* (John 3:16).   And *"If we confess our sins, He is faithful and just to forgive us our sins and to cleanse us from all unrighteousness."* (1 John 1:9) Yay!!

My Prayer: *"Dear Eloquent God, Thank You for sending your Son to die on the cross to save us, and for Your promise of eternal life in heaven! Your Word is a lamp unto my feet and a light unto my path. Your word IS "Life and Health." Please forgive me for my laziness in reading the Bible, and for my lack of faith in Your scripture promises. I declare that Your Word is My Food. I will turn to it for my guidance, wisdom, and basis of my faith. I love You Lord, my Provider of ALL food!"*
Love Your Daughter, Liz

Your Prayer and Reflection: How can you devote more time to studying God's Word? What Bible Verses can you commit to memory? Have you accepted Jesus as your Lord and Savior?

_____

_____

_____

"No One Sent Away"

"You do not have because you do not ask God."
— James 4:2

And no one who came to Jesus for healing was ever sent away...

John Tesh was given just 18 months to live. He had a rare form of prostate cancer and at one point looked at his wife, and said, "You have to kill me." John's bowels were paralyzed after his first surgery, and the chemo induced nausea was relentless. Later his cancer returned in his lymph nodes after battling the disease for 3 years. At this new diagnosis, doctors told Tesh they needed to radiate his pelvis with 62 radiation treatments over a period of three months.

Along with his actress wife, Connie Selleca, they decided John was *done* with medical treatments.

At that moment, his faith was re-activated through God's Word. They read and claimed Mark 11:23-24:

"Whatever you ask for in prayer believe that you'll receive it and you will have it."

Today, the Grammy-nominated composer and concert pianist is completely cancer free, a miracle he attributes to his faith in God and his supportive wife of 28 years. When his faith kicked into high gear he was healed of not just cancer, but arthritis as well.

Tesh documents his recovery in his memoir, *Relentless: Unleashing a Life of Purpose, Grit, and Faith.*

John Tesh realized that Jesus died on the cross not only for our sins, but that He also bore our sickness at the whipping post. During the course of Jesus' life no one was turned away who came to Him asking for healing.

John Tesh and the Author-Speaker Pastor Andrew Womack talk about the "Essentials for Healing." Here is a summary:

1. **It's God's Will for you to be healthy and whole.** Jesus says, *"I came to give you life in abundance."* God says He has *plans of hope and a future* for us. Proverbs 4:22 says, *"For they (God's Words) are life unto those that find them and health to all their flesh." "I will restore your health and heal your wounds,"* says the Lord. Jesus said to the Centurion, *"Go! It will be done as you believed it would."* And his servant was healed.

2. **Confess and repent of any sin.** Jesus says, *"Repent or perish,"* two times in the Bible.

James 5 says, *"Confess your faults to one another and pray for one another that you may be healed."* Scripture says, *"If we have iniquity in our heart God cannot hear our prayer."* So we must forgive others and lay any bitterness or unforgiveness at the foot of the cross. It is also essential that we ask God to forgive us for our shortcomings and turn from those sins. We need to be *SORRY* for our sins. If we stay in bad habits, sin, and rebellion then disease and the devil have an opening. John 5 says, "Sin no more, lest a worse thing happen." Make a change of mind, heart, and action. Ask God to reveal hidden sins.

3. **Pray to God, with the expectation that, "Whatever things you ask for when you pray, believe that you will receive them, and you will have them."** (Mark 11:24) We are to come boldly before the throne with our requests. Jesus said to the woman who touched His robe, "Your faith has made you whole, go in peace and be healed of your disease." In fact, "As many as touched Him were made well."

4. **Take authority over the sickness.** God word says, *"Resist the devil and he will flee"* and *"He who is in me is greater than that which is in the world."* Jesus says in Mark 16 "In my name they will cast out demons." God says that we have the same power in us that raised Jesus from the dead; the Holy Spirit power. We can speak to the disease, "I bind and cast out the spirit of cancer in Jesus' name! I bind the spirit of depression, leave now! I bind and rebuke the cancer,

ALL in the name of Jesus Christ." (See Matthew 18:18)

5. **Walk in faith, believing and receiving that you are healed.** James says, *"Faith without works is dead."* If we mope around, trust man and medication, are we walking in faith? Our actions and decisions need to reflect our faith in God's healing promises. It's crucial to study God's Word, eat it up and embody it. *"A double-minded man is unstable in all his ways."* Believe and receive your healing because of Jesus' act on the cross where He, *"bore our sickness and sins."* Claim the promise, *"I shall not die, but live, and declare the works of the Lord."* And *"By His stripes I am healed!"*

If you are having troubles making these leaps of faith, study God's Word in the Bible. God says, *"Faith comes by hearing, and hearing by the Word of God."* Also, as your faith becomes stronger and you embrace God's promises, your body may lag behind in the healing. There may be instantaneous healing or, it may take a bit of time. Remember the story where Jesus cursed the fig tree and it took a full day for the tree to die? With healing it may take time in a similar fashion.

Jesus Healed Them All

Many people came to Jesus for healing. When searching the Bible, I discovered that Jesus healed them *ALL*. He wants us to come with a humble heart and ask. Because of Jesus we can walk in divine health, both physically and spiritually.

Jesus *NEVER* sent anyone to a doctor for healing, not even to His disciple Luke, who was a "beloved physician." It gives us the thought to *pause* before procedure.

Jesus healed out of love and to fulfill what the prophet Isaiah said in the Old Testament, *"He Himself took our sickness and carried away our diseases."* (Matthew 8:16-17)

While Jesus was on His way to Jerusalem where He would be crucified, a blind man begging by the side of the road called out, *"Jesus, have mercy on me!"*

Jesus stopped and asked the man, *"What do you want me to do for you?"*

"Lord I want to see," he replied.

Jesus said to him, *"receive your sight; your faith has healed you."*

Jesus provides healing and forgiveness for us, through His finished work on the cross; God has not made this difficult to understand. The body, or bread, is for the physical healing of our bodies. The blood is for the forgiveness of our sins. We just need a *simple faith* that focuses on seeing Jesus and what He has already done for us.

Jesus First Strategy:
"Jesus never turns anyone away who comes to Him in faith."

Faith positions us for the resurrection power of God, which is more than enough to heal every kind of sickness and disease. With what Jesus did on the cross for us and God's extraordinary promises, what seems impossible is possible.

Our circumstances with serious illness are no match for the promises of God. It takes the faith of a mustard seed.

God's Will be Done

Many Christians only pray, "God's will be done," rather than asking, praying and crying out to God for miracles.

Well-meaning Christians often miss out on God's clear instructions in the Bible. God says *"The fervent prayers of the righteous are Powerful and Effective."* The Psalmist says, *"I cried to you for help, and You healed me."* He tells us we can do *"ALL things through Christ who strengthens us".* Maybe some pastors or Bible teachers avoid living in and teaching the miracles to protect themselves. They don't want to give Christians a bad name, in case there is not healing. Often, they don't pray for supernatural intervention, and therefore miracles or healing may or may not happen.

When people just pray for "God's Will to be done" it may also be to protect from the possibility of disappointment. Is there a lack of faith in God's ability, or willingness to heal? A sovereign God does not need us to protect Him. Remember He can do All Things, and He tells us WE can do all things through the Holy Spirit living within us. It's a lot to consider.

For me, I would rather err on the side of asking for complete healing, believing in His Promises. His word says that He promises 'hope and a future' – 'life in abundance' and 'healing'. God's will for us is *Health and Healing!*

This is the Day

Several years ago, my husband was called to play piano at a church event. He was amazed that the service consisted of one woman speaking on health and cancer. Her name was Dr. Lorraine Day; A best-selling author, she was also a Chief of Orthopedic Surgery at San Francisco General Hospital.

One day, Lorraine found a small tumor, the size of an almond on her chest. The biopsy determined that the tumor was cancer. Soon the tumor was the size of a grapefruit. Lorraine refused to have a mastectomy, chemotherapy, or radiation recommended by the doctors. She had witnessed firsthand the failures of conventional medicine.

She said, "Chemotherapy and radiation are poison, and doctors are deathly afraid of it for themselves." She was aware the first thing she needed to do was change her diet. She eliminated all animal proteins, with a new diet, but the tumor continued to grow larger and more painful.

Dr. Day tried everything, and nothing seemed to work. Bedridden for six months, at one point she was not expected to last through the night. But then she prayed to God for guidance and realized that *she* was responsible for developing the cancer! She explored every aspect of her life and turned to God for her healing. She had faith that He would not turn her away. Then in partnership with God, she developed a comprehensive plan allowing her body to heal.

Dr. Lorraine Day uses the acronym NEW START: Nutrition, Exercise, Water, Sunlight, Temperance, Air, Rest, Trust in God, Forgiveness, and Benevolence (meaning helping and thinking about others instead just oneself).

Don't Let Anyone Discourage You!

Dr. Day was completely healed by God and her only expense was organic food. New research shows that half of all cancer patients spend their **entire life savings** on cancer treatments. Sound familiar? Remember the woman in the Bible who spent all her money on physicians and grew not better but worse?

We cannot allow sowing any seeds of doubt. I keep my distance from people who doubt in God's healing. The Bible and its Promises are far above man's knowledge or medicine. Scriptures show God's healing through the One who works the impossible; Jesus.

There is **not one instance** in the Bible where someone was turned away by Jesus who came to him for healing.

Jesus First Strategy:
"Whatever you ask for in prayer, believe that you have received it, and it will be yours." (Matt 21:22)

"Everything is possible for the person who has faith," (Mark 9:23).

Jesus said to the Roman officer *"Go home and what you believe will be done for you."* And the officer's servant was healed at that very moment, (Matthew 8:13).

Jesus said *"Do you believe that I can heal you?"*

"Yes, sir!" they answered. Then Jesus touched their eyes and said, *"Let it happen, then, just as you believe!"* and their sight was restored, (Matthew 9:28-29).

However, in Jesus' home town where most folks did not believe in Him, He did not perform many miracles; He was able, but they did not ask for miracles or have faith. He dusted off His feet and moved on because of their unbelief.

My Friend Penny, posted a compelling testimony recently:
"I cannot go to sleep without giving the Lord some more praise! My right shoulder and spine have been on fire with pain this week. But as I've stayed in the promises of God's Word through the test—that He heals ALL. He has come through once again! That spot in my back is gone, and my shoulder has a dull ache that will go, as well.

No Doctors, no Meds—just Jesus. Thank You Lord! Your Word NEVER fails!!!"

She continued, "The way the Lord walked me through this was pulling His promises on healing out—reading them over and over and over until they were ingrained in my heart. When symptoms came, I would quote scripture. When Satan would try to whisper diagnoses, I spoke God's promises; *'The Lord will restore my health and heal my wounds.'"* (Jer. 30:17) What Penny said next blew my mind:

"Healing has to come, if we truly believe,
or His Word is a lie—and we know it is not.

So stand on the promises of God and do not let go until healing comes! I also prayed for my unbelief in the beginning."* Penny also mentioned that she calls a friend who has deep healing faith to pray and help bolster her faith. Our God is an awesome God!

My Prayer: *"Thank You God for loving us. You never sent anyone away who came and asked for healing. I will continue to trust You and petition for continued health in abundance. I am forever grateful!" Love Your Daughter, Liz*

Your Prayer and Reflection: How can you increase your faith and decrease doubt?

_____

_____

_____

*Penny's healing scripture reference:
https://www.biblestudytools.com/topical-verses/healing-bible-verses/

Hiking to waterfalls in the Blue Ridge Mountains

Go in Peace — *Song by: Eric Soldahl/K. Tunseth CCLI, ©2000*

Jesus met a woman at someone's home one night
She entered very quietly and waited out of sight
She then stood by the Savior, who was about to eat
The tears that tickled from her eyes, she used to wash his feet

Go in Peace your sins are forgiven
Go in Peace you've shown great love
Go in Peace your faith has saved you - Go in Peace and love

The woman was a sinner, the others told Him so
They seemed embarrassed by her act and wished that she would go
But Jesus said 'I tell you truth, the act that she has done,
Has shown her faith and love in me and proves her sins are gone'
Go in Peace your faith has saved you - Go in Peace and love.

Healing and Salvation

"Bless the LORD, O my soul, and forget not all His benefits: who forgives all your iniquities, who <u>heals all your diseases</u>, who redeems your life from destruction."—Psalm 103:2-4

The doctor pressed hard on my belly with the ultrasound probe. "Something is wrong, isn't it?" I said.

I could feel the bones of my baby girl pressing through the layers of my belly. I glanced at the ultrasound screen and she was frozen. My baby was dead.

I knew I was responsible for her death. What is the punishment for a mother like me? I thought.

A few days later, I delivered my baby in the middle of the night in the emergency room. She was born still, lifeless, and beautiful. The nurse placed my stillborn child in a mauve plastic, rectangular tub. She was curled up with her head bowed as if she was praying. It broke my heart.

In that moment, I began sobbing quietly, as they took my precious baby away. It was my job to take care of her, she was depending on me, and I let her down.

After the loss, the guilt was almost more than I could bear. During the pregnancy, I had even desired a miscarriage. My drinking and poor diet had contributed to the demise of my baby. I started taking antidepressants, but they didn't work. One night I woke up at the bottom of the stairs. I had fallen while searching for my baby. I was living in a fog.

After a year of despair, night terrors, and depression I found myself in church one day. It was a communion Sunday. As I raised the bread and cup to my mouth, a saving miracle occurred. Suddenly, a sweet angelic voice rang out from high in the choir loft. As this angel sang: *How Great Thou Art*, I remembered what I had learned as a little girl; Jesus died on the cross for my sins. I knew deep in my bones *I was forgiven*.

As tears streamed from my eyes, I realized that not only was I was forgiven for the poor choices during my pregnancy, but for everything else I had done wrong in my life. As I swallowed in communion, I knew that my baby was in a wonderful place and I would see her again in heaven.

"You made all the delicate inner parts of my body, and knit them together in my mother's womb," I read in my Bible later.

The loss of my baby Stephanie brought me back to Jesus. One morning, I prayed a prayer and renewed myself to God.

"Dear God, I'm so sorry for what I have done.
Thank you for loving me and changing my heart. I realize that
I fell short. Thank You for sending Jesus to die on the cross and
forgiving me for what I have done wrong with my pregnancy.

I humbly repent. Thank You for lifting me out of the pit of sadness and guilt. I recommit my life to You today. I know now that I will see my baby, Stephanie, in heaven someday. I love You. In Jesus name I pray, Amen."

That Sunday night I opened my Bible and the words jumped off the page, *"Though your sins are like scarlet, I will make them white as snow."*

My life has never been the same. I truly believe that I was "born again" on that bright Spring day in church. I had always believed in God but that day was a major turning point. After that transformation my priorities and values changed. I started rollerblading around Lake Merritt in downtown Oakland, California with a tambourine that said, *'Jesus Loves Us!'* I still have that tambourine today and use it while my husband and I travel around as musical missionaries.

Salvation and Communion

The more we see that God is both our *Spiritual* and *Physical* Healer, the more healing is released. Jesus heals by taking on our sin, sickness and pains. And our burdens.

We have one musical friend, Steve, who does communion everyday in his own home. I wonder what miracles we might see in our own lives if we followed Steve's example?

Could it be that we are leaving precious, God-given presents under the Christmas tree? The Bible seems clear:

"Take, eat; this is My Body which is broken for you; do this in remembrance of Me." (1 Corinthians 11:24)

"This cup is the new covenant in My blood. This do, as often as you drink it, in remembrance of Me." (1 Corinthians 11:25)

In the 'Bible app' on my phone, there is a Bible Study "Plan" on **Healing.** It is a 21-day Healing Bible Study, called, "The Lord Who Heals You." I recommend this study VERY highly. The twenty-first day of the Bible Study the author talks about communion.

Here is an excerpt:

"Jesus' body was 'broken' with sin, sickness and disease, and every time that we take the bread in Communion we are to remember, or meditate on the fact that 'surely He bore our sicknesses and carried our pains' and receive by faith the healing that He has provided for us." (Isaiah 53:4)

The cup represents His blood for atonement for our sins. *And the bread represents His body where He bore our sickness and disease.*

Why Are Some Healed and Others Not?

Some nights when Eric and I are at our home, we search for Bible-based programs on TV. Many shows feature true life miracles and testimonies. One host answers questions that viewers have submitted. A viewer posed this question:

"Why do some people get healed and others don't?"

The host thoughtfully responded by explaining,

"If your heart doesn't condemn you, then you have confidence before the Lord." He paused and peered into the camera saying, "But, if you have iniquity in your heart, then God cannot hear your prayer." Iniquity meaning unforgiveness and unrepented sin.

Remember the Bible verse in James, that says,

"Confess your faults to one another and pray for one

another that ye may be healed. For the fervent prayers of the righteous are powerful and effective."

Sometimes the hidden sin in our life stops Kingdom healing. It may be unconscious or un-confessed sin. Often when there is a sin kept in secret, such as maliciousness, jealousy or even porn, then healing may be thwarted.

Satan often blinds us from realizing an unrepented sin such as pride, succumbing to anxiety or depression, gluttony, drunkenness, lying, unforgiveness, making children our idol, greed, gossiping, and covetousness.

Maybe we are putting our faith in doctors and pharmaceuticals above God. Maybe we are begging for physical healing but making poor choices for our bodies. Remember, God gives us *"free will"* and unfortunately, there may be negative consequences for our poor decisions.

Sometimes we pray fervently for a loved one and the healing doesn't happen. It may be that the person we are praying for is not in agreement with our prayer, or has iniquity in their heart. We need to pray in obedience.

Confessing our faults and repenting, allows us to come boldly before God with confidence, releasing *Kingdom flow*. In John 16:23 Jesus says, *"I assure you: Anything you ask the Father in My name, He will give you."*

To pray in Jesus' name implies an intimate and personal relationship with Jesus. The closer we are to Him and His Word, the more our desires match up; *Teamwork.*

Sometimes there is immediate healing. I've noticed that sometimes people pray for years before healing happens. Sometimes the healing is immediate but our body takes a little time to catch up. It is God's timing, not ours.

Natalie's Fall

One Sunday afternoon Eric and I hiked to a beautiful waterfall lookout point. As we gazed at God's beauty and gushing falls, we heard screams. An 18-year-old girl fell from the top of the Twin Falls, dropping 75 feet into a shallow granite pool.

Eric and I rushed up the side of the granite, where a retired fire fighter and nurse pulled her out of the shallow water.

I cradled this young girl, who had blunt force trauma on her head and face. I prayed fervently over her for healing. Eric found a few towels and called for others to help. A young ER doctor joined us on the ledge but he said there was nothing we could do except make her comfortable.

I begged for God to heal her. I recited scripture and I believed that God would heal her. As she lay unconscious in shock, I pleaded with the Lord. "Restore her health and heal her wounds, Lord!"

As her breathing got shallower, I spoke directly to her:

"Jesus loves you sweetie. God loves you so much, that He sent His son Jesus to die on the cross for your sins, and if you believe in Him you will have everlasting life in heaven…"

What happened next was a miracle; Natalie lifted her head and chest an inch! Kissing her arm, I whispered *"Jesus loves you."* Then her body went limp. She seemed at peace. This sweet young girl died before the first responders arrived. The ER doctor said the internal bleeding was just too much.

We did our best to console her close friend, Maria, who stood by sobbing. It was heart-breaking and all were shaken. Afterward we prayed with Maria in the Twin Falls parking lot.

That night, Eric and I prayed in bed as we always do and said extra fervent prayers for Natalie, Maria, and her family and friends. In the wee hours of the next morning Eric gently nudged me and shared a powerful dream he had:

"Natalie was at the base of the waterfall, and two angels flew down and picked her up—one under each arm—then they lifted her up over the waterfall toward heaven! Her body and face were perfect and beautiful."

I truly believe Natalie is with Jesus in Heaven, dancing with my baby Stephanie in fields of colorful wild flowers.

Eric and I plan to place warning signs at the trail head and base of the waterfall in Natalie's honor.

Roadblocks, Healing and God's Promises

After this experience I had new questions about faith.

"Why don't we always get the healing that we pray for," I asked my husband? As I have grappled with this question, I realized that we don't get to know all the answers on this side of heaven. Because of sin in the world we do have sickness and tragic accidents. In Natalie's case, she had severe blunt trauma to her head. She died tragically as I prayed for her.

I believe Natalie was healed spiritually, but not physically; that she now has a healed body in Heaven and I will see her again someday. Scripture says, *"The Lord will deliver me into His heavenly kingdom."* God's ways are higher than our ways. No matter *what* we trust Him.

Since we are in relationship with God, our actions do matter. Sometimes there are physical or spiritual roadblocks that hinder healing. There are bad habits, hang-ups and hurts.

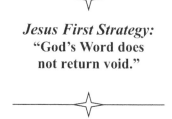

Jesus First Strategy:
**"God's Word does
not return void."**

I recently came across a posting from a woman that has been in healing ministry for 27 years. In a nutshell she explained:

"Jesus ALREADY provided healing at the cross for us, just like salvation. By His stripes you WERE healed is Peter looking back at the cross. Isaiah looks forward to the cross. **The word HEALED in the original means: to cure, heal**."

She continued with her biblical explanation, "We must APPROPRIATE (secure) our healing and our salvation. It is not instant to everyone. **We must look at the Word of God and BELIEVE what it says.** God's Word does not return void." Sometimes our bodies take time to physically *catch up* with the spiritual healing that has occurred. She explained: "It is important to note the roadblocks to healing. Occasionally, we have issues on *OUR* part that block healing."

Finally, she elaborated, "The major roadblocks are: Unforgiveness, unrepented sin, lack of faith, doubt, habitual sin, fear, unbelief, complaining, abusing one's body, not breaking demonic strongholds, family sin, bitterness, trusting man or medicine over God." Unfortunately, most pastors do not even discuss, or list the specific sins, that often block restoration. But scripture is clear: *"Do not be deceived: Neither the sexually immoral, nor idolaters, nor adulterers, nor those whose practice homosexuality, nor sodomites, nor thieves, nor the greedy, nor drunkards, nor revilers, nor swindlers, will inherit the Kingdom of God."* (1 Chron. 6:9-11)

We can address these roadblocks and have access to healing, as promised by God. Exodus 15:26 reinforces this concept: *"If you do what is right in His eyes and keep His statutes..."* then the Lord continues with a promise: *"I will put none of the diseases on you...I am the Lord your healer!"*

We must ask in faith, without doubting. He who doubts is like a wave in the sea tossed by the wind.

A woman had been disabled by a spirit for eighteen years. She was hunched over and could not stand up straight. When Jesus saw her, He said, *"**Woman, you are set free from your infirmity.**"* Then He laid His hands on her, and immediately she straightened up and began to glorify God. She had faith.

God instructs us to pray with great faith, remove roadblocks, ask for the healing, never give up, don't doubt, and trust Him! Believe in His healing promises!

My Prayer: *"Dear God, thank You for sending Your Son Jesus to die on the cross for our sins. Once again, thank You for washing me clean and healing my body!" Love Liz*

Your Prayer and Reflection: Have you received the Final Healing of Salvation through Jesus? (Refer to Chapter 8 for the steps.) What stumbling blocks to healing can you work on removing?

_____

_____

_____

Overcoming "Dis" ease and Depression

*"Be strong and of good cheer. Do not be afraid,
or be dismayed."*—2 Chronicles 32:7

𝐴 few years ago I was going through months and months of super heavy perimenopausal bleeding—I mean gushing until I was severely anemic. During this time, depression and anxiety had started to slip in. I found it hard to find joy in my life.

One day a friend, Judy, came to visit me. She shared her harrowing experience of enduring three surgeries in five months. My friend spoke of her surgeries, anxieties, repentance, and of God's love and forgiveness. Judy explained that she needed to ask the Lord to forgive her.

Judy had been filled with doubts and fears. "Doubts and fears often creep into us," she explained, "but we have a choice as to how we respond."

Judy asked God to forgive her. Then she refocused her thoughts 'taking them captive to Christ', and things changed drastically for her. Her health improved and her depression lifted.

Jesus First Strategy:
One Definition of Disease:
"Dis" = *absence of,*
"Ease" = *Peace*

Here is the prayer I prayed after Judy's inspiring testimony. "Please forgive me Lord for choosing to wallow in depression and anxiety. I repent! Help me Lord!"

I clung to a verse reciting it whenever fear and depression crept in, *"He who has begun a good work in me will carry it on to completion until the day of Christ Jesus."*

Depression/Anxiety

"Anxiety in the heart of man causes depression, but a good word makes it glad." (Proverbs 12:25)

Personally, I have suffered with anxiety and depression at times over the years. I have turned to pharmaceuticals, including Paxil and Lexapro. Paxil caused me to be so tired that I would drop my daughters off at school, come home, and go back to bed. I was self-employed as an interior designer so I had the flexibility to do that.

The Pharma drug, Lexapro, caused me anxiety because somewhere deep in my heart I knew I should not be on it. What I needed, was to face the issues behind the depression and anxiety.

Anti-depressants are mind and mood-altering drugs. They mask symptoms of underlying problems. Also, pharmaceutical anti-depressants can have serious side effects that can include suicidal thoughts, weight gain and personality change; recent studies have shown that;
Anti-depressants fail to cure the 'root' of major depression.

When we have anxiety or depression sometimes it is God trying to get our attention to deal with an issue in our heart. Maybe it is unforgiveness, maybe it is anger, maybe it is sloth, jealously, gluttony, drunkenness, anxiety...I have found that Christian Counseling has helped get to the 'root' of my anxiety and depression issues. I have also found that the natural supplement, St. John's Wort is a natural anti-depressant which helps increase Serotonin levels (which are often low when depressed). Studies show that St. John's Wort is as effective as standard antidepressants, and the herb has fewer side effects. Please research amounts before taking.

It seems much easier to take a pill rather than acknowledge a sinful pattern or deep issue that needs to be addressed. Anxiety and depression in themselves are not a sin. These feelings may crop up for us when faced with difficult situations or when the 'enemy' attacks. How *we respond to these attacks can be sinful or not.*

Allowing ourselves to settle in with depression and anxiety goes against Jesus' commandment to us.

In Matthew Chapter 6, Jesus counsels us not to be anxious:

- *"Therefore I tell you, do not be anxious about your life, what you will eat or drink..."*
- *"And which of you by being anxious adds a single hour to his span of life?"* – *"Therefore, do not be anxious..."*

A fellow Jesus follower recently shared her clever analogy; **"Black birds of fear, anxiety and depression can fly around us. However, they can't nest on our heads unless we allow it..."**

We can face anxiety head on, by washing our mind with God's Word, fervent prayer and singing praises. God promises to deliver us.

Verses that have helped me are:

- *"Cast your burdens upon the Lord and He will sustain you."* (Psalm 55:22)
- *"Whatever things are true, noble, just, pure, lovely, of good report, virtuous, or praiseworthy – meditate on these things."* (Philippians 4:8-9)
- *"Be anxious for nothing but in all things with prayer and supplication with Thanksgiving let your petitions be known to God, and the peace of God that surpasses all understanding will guard your heart and minds in Christ Jesus."* (Philippians 4:6-7)
- *"Be strong and of good courage. Do not be afraid or dismayed!"* (2 Chron. 32:7-8)
- *"God has not given us a spirit of fear, but of power, love and sound mind."* (2 Timothy 1:7)

When we have continual anxiety, it is because we are not trusting God enough. We are trusting in ourselves more than God. Again, the best way to trust God more is to immerse ourselves in prayer and in God's Promises. Singing helps too!

It seems like just yesterday; Eric and I attended the SING Conference in Nashville, hosted by Keith and Kristyn Getty. With over 10,000 believers, we joined in their powerful song, "*In Christ Alone, my Hope is Found.*"

One remarkable evening while there, we sang at the Grand Ole Opry. Joni Eareckson Tada led the packed house in a Hymn Sing Along from her wheelchair. At the age of 17 she became paralyzed from the shoulders down after diving head-first into a lake. This courageous lady told us that someone once asked her, 'Won't it be nice to be in heaven with a new body?' and she said, 'yes, but even better, I look forward to a new heart, with a new attitude.'

Overcoming with Spiritual Warfare

After the night at the Opry, I realized that a repentant heart along with spiritual warfare is needed to overcome fear and anxiety. Depression seems to be an on-going battle for most women. It helped me to engage the Deliverance Minister to be released of demonic influence. Consistent work has been needed to combat anxiety, and depression.

In my book *Floored and Delivered,* I share the entire process of my deliverance. When we are afraid, anxious, or depressed, we can fight back. It is called *Spiritual Warfare.* One friend prays out loud with God's Authority,

"Devil you are NOT welcome here and you need to remove yourself from here! I am a child of the most High King!"

Marijuana, alcohol, and legal or illegal drugs can open a person up to demonic influence and or possession. Marijuana and alcohol may mask a person's problems by adjusting oneself mentally to cope with things they do not have the skills to cope with.

When we turn to drugs or alcohol we are sometimes hoping for healing without repentance, or healing without dealing with the underlying problem. God calls us to confess our faults, work through the issues, and pray to be healed.

Natural Remedies for Anxiety and Depression

- Lavender, chamomile, and frankincense oils.
- Supplements: Fish oil-high in EPA. Vitamin D.
- St. John's Wort capsules – this is a natural anti-depressant used throughout Europe. It's cheap.
- Magnesium is known as the "relaxation mineral."
- Prayer, Meditation and Reciting Scripture.
- Singing! -you can't be depressed singing praise songs.
- Exercise, sleep, and forgiveness.
- 20-30 minutes of sunshine daily.

Home Remedy for Anxiety, Healing Bath Salts:
-Combine 3 cups of Epsom salt and 1 cup of baking soda. Add 1 cup of the dry ingredients and 20 to 30 drops of lavender to warm bath water. Soak for 20 to 30 minutes.
Home Remedy for Depression: Invigorating Inhalation:
-Rub a few drops of lavender oil, or ylang ylang, oil into your hands and cup your mouth and nose and breathe in slowly. Helps with sleep too.

Gratitude

Gratitude is a big factor in lifting depression. New research shows that you can "rewire" your brain to be happy by simply recalling 3 things you're grateful for every day for 21 days!

A few years ago my Mother-in-law was going through a season of slight depression and sadness; still referring back to losing her husband after a lifetime together. My sister-in-law suggested that every morning, she write down three things for which she was grateful. After just a couple of weeks Moma reported that her outlook was much more joyful and positive!

Corrie ten Boom, the Holocaust Survivor, wrote one of the most powerful books I have ever read, called *The Hiding Place*. After World War II and surviving the Nazi concentration camps, she often said: *"If you look at the world, you'll be distressed. If you look within, you'll be depressed. But if you look to Christ, you'll be at rest."*

Christian Counseling and Forgiveness

Over the years, I have turned to Christian Counselors on several occasions. I have found it most helpful. There are "Stephen Ministers," who are lay counselors in many communities, who counsel for free. Proverbs says, there is safety in a multitude of counselors. Faith-based Counseling allows a safe space to process bitterness and unforgiveness. Unforgiveness has been shown to cause disease.

In order to be released from depression, we may need to cleanse ourselves of unforgiveness towards others. Sometimes we need to forgive ourselves, as well.

- Forgiveness is choosing *not* to hold an offense against someone.
- Forgiveness is choosing *not* to dwell on the offense, or continue to rehearse it in your mind.
- Forgiveness is choosing *not* to keep a record (or keep score). It's trusting God with the situation.

Sometimes it is hard to forgive others who have done us wrong. Forgiveness does not mean that what the other person did was right, or okay; *forgiveness does not require reconnection.* It's okay to avoid toxic or abusive people.

Forgiveness is a very important component to healing. When we harbor resentments, bitterness, annoyance, grudges, and unforgiveness our prayers may not be heard by God and it is harder to hear God's voice.

One of my favorite books is called, *Boundaries* by Townsend and Cloud. Setting healthy limits and boundaries are a gift to the other person and ourselves. Boundaries bind up the bad behavior.

Jesus First Strategy:
"God will not forgive us, unless we forgive others…"

One sign of forgiveness is: **"Feeling more sorry for the other person than ourselves."** When we forgive ourselves and others, we gain freedom.

Duke University studied the characteristics of happiness. In their research, they found that there were eight attributes that lead to happiness, *Four* of them had to with forgiveness and releasing resentment.

As Jesus followers, we are called to be an example by forgiving others quickly and *"not to be easily offended."*

Jesus says, "And whenever you stand praying, if you have anything against anyone, forgive him, that your Father in heaven may also forgive your trespasses...if you do not forgive, neither will your Father in heaven forgive your trespasses." (Mark 11:25-26)

My Prayer: *"Thank You God for helping me overcome disease, I feel great! Forgive me when I allow depression or anxiety to slip in. Please cast those demons and thoughts away from me. I vow to replace those negative thoughts with Your Great Words and natural remedies. Also help me to forgive others quickly! I love You God, Jesus and Holy Spirit."*
Love Your Daughter, Liz

Your Prayer and Reflection: What Bible Verse can you claim when you feel anxious or depressed? What natural remedies can you implement to ward off depression?

_____

_____

_____

"Sing" Conference in Nashville. Singing chases away the blues!

Prayer and Fasting

"I humbled my soul with fasting"— Psalm 69:10
"This kind does not go out except by prayer and fasting."
— Matthew 17:21

The power of prayer cannot be underestimated! Scientists are discovering what believers have always known. Dr. Larry Dossey, M.D. of the National Institute of Health wrote an article called, Does *Prayer Heal*? The article reveals an amazing story and some compelling statistics.

During his residency, he had a patient with terminal lung cancer. Whenever he stopped by the man's bedside, there were members from the patient's church singing and praying by him. He thought, *soon they will be praying at his funeral*.

A year later, someone asked the doctor to see the old lung cancer patient. He couldn't believe this man was still alive.

Remarkably, the man's lungs were completely clear and all cancer was gone.

After this, the doctor researched and discovered several studies that showed that prayer brings about significant changes in physical conditions.

The most convincing study was by a cardiologist named Dr. Randolph Byrd conducted in 1988;

"A computer assigned 393 patients at the coronary care unit either to a group that was prayed for or not. The prayer groups were given the patients' first names and medical problems and asked to pray for the patients. When the study was completed 10 months later the prayed for patients benefited in several significant areas:

- They were five times less likely to require antibiotics.
- They were 2½ times less likely to suffer congestive heart failure.
- They were less likely to suffer cardiac arrest."

Wouldn't it be interesting to see world-wide statistics showing the correlation between prayer and healing?

Prayers Activate God's Power

If we are interwoven in a relationship with God our prayer will be the same as God's Will. In other words, God's desires will match ours. That's why in Mark 11:24, He says,

"Ask anything, and believing you shall receive it."

If we are not in a close relationship with God, we may not have that faith and confidence that is needed as we pray. Having a constant trust and communication with God is so imperative! God desires a faithful prayer relationship with us.

Remember: *"And the prayer of faith shall save the sick,"* **according to James 5:15.**

Persistent prayer is "key". Remember the parable Jesus taught in Luke 18 about the widow who kept going to the judge over and over begging for justice. Jesus says,

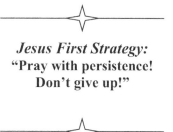

Jesus First Strategy:
"Pray with persistence! Don't give up!"

"Will not God bring justice for His chosen ones who cry out day and night?"

So don't give up! Start praying and keep praying.

Intercessory prayer, meaning praying for others, is powerful and effective as well. One of my "Moms in Prayer" partners, Rose, was diagnosed with breast cancer several months ago. She decided to have surgery, a single mastectomy, after much prayer. The week before surgery she had great peace, however, had moments of fear as well, just like I did before my surgery.

On the day of surgery my other two prayer partners and I prayed for Rose, and just like the story in the Bible, we envisioned ourselves going on the rooftop and lowering down our dear friend, Rose, to Jesus. We all prayed and fasted for her that day.

We had faith that Jesus would heal her through the surgery. We did not doubt. We stood in the gap for any doubts or fears she may have had. True to form, God showed His glory and miracles with this healing of Rose.

Fasting from Food!?

Do we make food an idol? Sometimes I obsess over my next meal or I overindulge with snacks. Matthew 6:25 says:

"Therefore I tell you, do not worry about your life, what you will eat or drink; or about your body, or what you will wear. Is not life more than food, and the body more than clothes?"

The 1st commandment is, *"Have no other God's before me."* That includes food. Have we made food a god? Are we more excited about our next meal than we are about Jesus?

My dear friend Jamelle says, "sometimes we need to fast so that God may put a word in our mouth, instead of food." Sometimes fasting gives us courage and God's Favor. In the Bible days it wasn't *if* they fasted it was **when** they fasted. And remember, Jesus fasted for forty days and forty nights.

One Bible story shows a famous fasting miracle:

Queen Esther asked her people to fast with her **for three days** before going to the King, to plead with him to save her people; the people of God, Israel.

After the 'group fast', she put on her best adornment and went before the King under the possible penalty of death.

"If I perish, I perish," she said.

Esther's mission was to save the Hebrew nation. Her mission was more important than her own life, or meals for three days. Esther found favor with the King when they met together, and an entire nation was saved! This story shows how *prayer and fasting activates God's power*.

A Sundown Fast

My husband Eric was suffering for two weeks straight with an inner ear problem. His ear felt like it was continually plugged and there was possibly fluid behind the blockage. It was hard for my always happy Hubby to stay up-beat all the time with this pain.

We prayed about whether or not to go to the doctor or continue the natural remedies. We did more online research and the possible surgery suggested sounded very dramatic, very painful, and was only a 50% success rate. We continued to pray for guidance and on day 14, Eric heard a word from God,

"Fast today."

Eric shared his message with me, and we both decided to do a sun down fast: water only till dinner. Whenever we got hungry, we dropped to our knees and prayed for healing and recited scripture for his painful blocked ear.

Later at bedtime, his ear was still plugged and hurting, but during the night God touched his ear. He woke up the next morning with a completely clear ear. His hearing had returned and the pain was gone.

Immediately, we dropped to our knees alongside the bed. We thanked God for His Mercy and for responding to our prayer and fasting.

My eyes have been opened to the physical benefits of fasting as well. I have been gulping down research studies and scientific evidence that proves over and over the healthy side effects of fasting.

Data on Fasting

The scientific evidence shows that by water fasting for three to five days it causes defective, cancerous, and old cells to **die off**. Even cancer stem cells die off as they are not getting fed. **Once a person breaks the fast and begins eating again, brand new stronger cells are created.**

These new cells boost our immunity and can help in healing the body. Paul and Patricia Bragg's book called, *Bragg Healthy Lifestyle*, gives a detailed explanation of how to safely conduct a fast. Fasting also helps detoxify the body and purge it of toxic poisons, viruses, and bacteria. When you feel a cold, illness, depression, or allergy attack coming on; fast. Fasting can also help reverse the aging process. We can live longer happier lives and just fasting 3 days a month will do it.

***Jesus First Strategy*:**
**"Jesus fasted for forty days and
forty nights –
Can we do a day or
two...or a morning?"**

According to Patricia and Paul Bragg, *"A peaceful, well planned distilled water fast is our favorite. This fast can cleanse your body of excess mucus, old fecal matter, trapped cellular, non-food wastes and help remove inorganic mineral deposits and sludge from your pipes and joints. Fasting works by self-digestion. During a fast your body will perform cleansing miracles by intuitively decomposing and burning only the substances and tissues that are damaged, diseased or unneeded, such as abscesses, tumors, excess fat and excess water and the stored (stock piled) congestive wastes!*

Vitamin C and grape-seed extract are both important if you are detoxifying from prescription drugs or alcohol overload."

Intermittent Fasting

Intermittent fasting; eating for 8 hours and fasting for 16 hours is also a very powerful detoxifying tool and can be done daily or once a week to help cleanse the body. I find that when I drink my apple cider vinegar concoction in the morning, my appetite is suppressed till lunch.

So intermittent fasting has become somewhat of a routine in my life. Jesus fasted for forty days and forty nights. Fasting has amazing physical results but is also a spiritual exercise, voluntary restraint from food for the purpose of seeking God. *The Miracle of Fasting*, by Paul and Patricia Bragg is another excellent resource to encourage you with fasting in your life. There are 25 verses in the Bible indicating why we should fast.

God wants a relationship with us, He doesn't want religion. He wants us to talk with Him, listen to Him and work with Him. He wants us to be obedient. For me, given my history with 3 cancers, He has put it on my heart to continue most days with intermittent fasting, and once a month a 3 day fast. I drink a lot of water with lemon.

I wonder what our lives would look like if we prayed and fasted like Esther or Daniel?

In the Bible we read about two specific fasts that Daniel followed. During the first *fast* he only ate vegetables and water to set himself apart for God. For a second fast, Daniel stopped eating meat, wine and other rich foods.

Daniel's Fast

"Please test your servants for ten days and let them give us vegetables to eat and water to drink." (Daniel 1:12)

Daniel ate no delicacies and abstained from meat and wine.

Daniel's *'Fast Food'* List:

- Water – (distilled is best)
- Almond milk, coconut water, and vegetable juice
- Vegetables – fresh or cooked, may be frozen (Organic)
- Fruits – apples, berries, cherries and citrus fruits and stone fruits (Organic)
- Whole grains including brown rice, oats, quinoa
- Beans & Legumes
- Nuts & seeds – raw, sprouted or dry roasted

Jesus First Strategy: **"A Three Day Water Fast has been shown to reset the entire immune system!"**

Consider a fast from; Fast Food, sugar, alcohol and soda.

In the beginning, the Lord gave us *food for thought*: Genesis 1:29 says: *"I give you every seed-bearing plant on the face of the whole earth and every tree that has fruit with seed in it. They will be yours for food."* **So in effect God was telling us right from the start to eat our fruits and vegetables**!

Benefits of Fasting

- Gives the body a physiological rest.
- It's the quickest way to lose weight (up to 10 pounds in the first week).
- Renews your faith and trust in God.

- Prayer and Fasting activates God's power.
- Defective cells starved – resets the immune system.
- Is used successfully in the treatment of many physical illnesses.
- Lowers and normalizes cholesterol and blood pressure levels.
- Increases pleasure of eating healthy foods.
- Purges the mucus, toxins, and arterial plaque.
- Often leads to a more vigorous marital relationship.
- Can eliminate drug and drinking addictions.
- Can train the body to consume food as needed.
- Saves time spent marketing, preparing and eating.
- Is routine for most of the animal kingdom.
- Under proper conditions is absolutely safe.
- Helps break addiction to sugar.
- Improves skin health.
- Decreases brain fog.
- Saves money.

You may feel a little "crummy" during parts of the fast, but hang in there because it is worth the long-term benefits. When I fast, I often feel little stabbing pangs of pain in my lower gut. I understand that fasting starves cancer, and I often imagine that any defective cells are dying off and are screaming in pain as they melt away. After completing a fast, I feel so good physically, and I am amazed at the miracles I many- times witness! All Glory and credit to God!

My Prayer: *"Thank You God for the miracles through prayer and fasting. Please give me extra obedience and self-control to pray and fast more often. I want a closer relationship with You. I love You!"* Love Your Daughter, Liz

Your Prayer and Reflection: What would help you to pray and fast more often?

_____

_____

_____

13

God's Food
And Other Remedies

"So whether you eat or drink, or whatever you do, do it all for the Glory of God." — 1 Corinthians 10:31

*O*ur dear friend Susan had a double mastectomy from invasive breast cancer. She followed up with chemotherapy and radiation. One day Eric and I spotted Susan and her husband while we were on a neighborhood walk. They pulled over in their car to deliver a "Holy Spirit" message,

"The doctor told me to lose excess fat around my waist because fat is full of estrogen and many cancers are fed by estrogen." Later, we saw Susan at a church potluck with her plate full of sweets and carbs and realized she struggled with her eating, even after her cancer scare.

Sadly, Susan died a year later as her breast cancer resurfaced in other areas of her body. I hope to be a messenger for my dear friend Susan and spread that word of truth she gave to me: *To lose the fat*. I want to honor her memory. After Susan's death, my husband and I made a commitment to eat healthier and exercise more.

One day we visited my friend, Olivia Angeli, a Holistic Nutritionist. We hired her to help our family with healthy eating. She met us at the Sprouts grocery store. She gave each of our sons a small grocery cart and coached them on the perils of buying unhealthy processed foods and drinks. Aisle by aisle we shopped. She asked them to read labels to pick out the foods they might enjoy eating that were still full of healthy or organic nutrition. They each selected favorite healthy foods for snacks and for a meal they prepared for the family once a week.

"When you are at the grocery store read the **front** of the food package for the <u>advertising</u> and read the **ingredient list** on the **back** for the <u>truth</u>," Olivia informed us.

"Eat to live, don't live to eat."

We recently saw a presentation by Dr. Steven Gundry, M.D. who wrote a book called: *The Longevity Paradox: How to Die Young at a Ripe Old Age*, and *The Plant Paradox Made Easy*. He talked about how more people are living to be 100 years or more. On the following page, are Gundry's top tips:

The Key Points for Longevity are:

1. Stay active. Studies show that people that live in mountainous and hilly areas, live longer. They get their heart rate up by walking or running on the neighborhood hills.
2. Do not eat processed or fast food (they are filled with toxins, sodium, sugar and preservatives).
3. Avoid prescription drugs when at all possible. The longest living people are on very few or no pharmaceutical drugs.
4. Expect that you are going to stay healthy and live long!
5. Stay positive!
6. Eat a low sugar diet.
7. Support a healthy "gut" with nutrition and lifestyle – *Our gut bacteria largely determine our health over the years.* Our intestinal flora can feed or fight cancer, Alzheimer's, arthritis, weight gain, skin tone, diabetes, mood, energy, anxiety, and depression. *Eighty percent of our overall health originates from our gut health.*

Dr. Gundry said he had never worked with a type 2 diabetic or a person with high cholesterol who he could not help reverse these aliments through diet and lifestyle choices.

My mother-in-law is a great example of living a long healthy life. She turned 95 this year. Last time we visited her in the San Francisco Bay area (which is a very hilly area ☺) I asked her,

"Moma, what do you attribute your long life to?"

She responded,

"It's God."

As I probed deeper, she revealed more of her secrets.

Moma hasn't had a drop of alcohol for many years; she eats

pretty healthy, and always orders the half portions at her retirement community. And most of all she trusts God with everything. She lives a pretty laid back, peaceful life. She is the one who writes down three things every morning that she is grateful for. She also enjoys treats now and then, and gets in a fair amount of walking to burn it off.

Last time we visited her she told me she didn't think she had much of a purpose left in life. Eric and I told her about the movie *War Room*, where the main character was a mighty warrior for God and created a prayer closet/war room in her home. She prayed in that war room often, doing spiritual battle, interceding for family and friends. It inspired her to start a prayer wall after hearing that story. Now every time we call Moma, she tells us about her prayer wall, and how she prays for one row of people on the wall every day. We told her,

"Moma, you have a <u>very</u> important job... it's your prayer wall."

It helps to have a purpose in life, especially in old age.

"They shall still bring forth fruit in old age...they are always healthy and fresh." (Psalm 92:14)

Water

Water is such an important part of the health picture. I have been combing through the book, *Water—the Shocking Truth that can Save your Life,* by Paul and Patricia Bragg. Purified water is essential for health and healing. Fluoride, chlorine and inorganic matter in water are the **enemies**. Fluoride and Chlorine are in tap water.

One solution is to drink distilled, filtered or spring water in BPA-Free bottles. We run our tap water through the *Zero Water* filter pitcher, which is a good solution; however, we are also looking into a countertop water distiller. The Braggs Water book suggests *Waterwise* distillers, or Berkey water filters.

According to several medical studies, **fluoridated, chlorinated tap water causes** many **health problems**.

One nurse we know in a Retirement Community said, "Most people lose their thirst-taste-buds as they get older. They shrivel up and get disease and die from dehydration, nothing more..."

Benefits of 8 glasses of distilled/ purified water per day:

- Weight loss
- Clears arteries
- Detoxifies body
- Reduces headaches
- Improves complexion
- Improves digestion
- Increases energy
- Helps with healthy hair, skin, nails, bones and joints
- Clears sludge in brain

Note: A squeeze of lemon, or 1 teaspoon of baking soda per day in the water will help alkalize the body. It fights disease.

Food as Medicine

On his death bed, Steve Jobs of Apple computer said: ***"Eat food as your medicine otherwise you'll have to eat medicine as your food."*** My brother-in-law knew him from the computer business. Both died about the same time relying on chemotherapy and other drugs. Confucius and Hippocrates echo the sentiment: *"Let food be thy medicine and medicine be thy food."*

"Eat Food as your Medicine, otherwise you will have to eat medicine as your Food."

In the Holy Scriptures it says, *"I urge you ... in view of God's mercy, to offer your bodies as a living sacrifice."* Also, *"In Christ we, though many, form one body, and each member belongs to all the others".* So as an obligation to our fellow believers we need to do our best to take care of our bodies. No guilt here, just a strong encouragement. As the body of Christ, we need each other to stay healthy and be an example to others.

Healthy Eating Interview

The following is an interview with a dear friend Kathleen who has been studying and practicing health and nutrition for over forty years. She was a drummer on our worship team in Tahoe California and a practicing attorney. She is an excellent example of putting a healthy lifestyle into practice. Many of the concepts listed below combined with the Forgiving *Plant Based*, Keto Lifestyle makes a great strategy.

I encourage you to create your own "do-able" lifetime eating plan. Crash diets don't work. For your health and the health of your family, start now. The interview is as follows:

Liz: "You've been doing the plant based macrobiotic diet for thirty years, is that right? And what motivates you to eat so healthy?

Kathleen: "Actually, for forty years I have been studying and working on becoming healthier. My parents ate the SAD Diet (Standard American Diet), and I knew it wasn't good. I am currently doing a combination of the modified Macrobiotic Diet, plant-based Keto with very limited animal protein and dairy. I do eat wild fish and limited grass fed and grass finished beef. I go every year to a health camp and once when there I met with Dr. Gundry who wrote three awesome books.

Liz: "What do you think about organics and GMO's?"

Kathleen: "Organics are best for all food. GMO's are bad for you. They've genetically modified the plants so they produce extra toxins to repel insects. These toxins are called lectins. These lectins can also be toxic to humans and may have ill health effects. Organics are worth the little extra money."

Liz: "What foods do you recommend eating? And what foods do you recommend avoiding?"

Kathleen: "No wheat, corn or soy, no processed foods, no refined sugars or high fructose corn syrup."

Kathleen continued: "I avoid white rice, white pasta, dairy, and white flour. **If God made it, it is good to eat... and if man made it, it is not!**

Brown rice soaked overnight and cooked in a pressure cooker is a basic in my kitchen. Lots of legumes, soaked overnight and quinoa, soaked overnight to remove the lectins. I recommend eating a lot of fermented products.

Fermented foods include: sauerkraut, kimchi, pickles, and kombucha. These foods may also reduce heart disease risks and aid in digestion, immunity, and weight loss.

I also eat a lot of plant-based fats and other healthy fats including nuts, seeds, coconut and olive oil, and lots of vegetables including broccoli and cauliflower, spinach and other leafy greens. Oatmeal, honey and pure maple syrup are okay; in fact, I am making some cookies right now!"

Liz: "A final question; How do you handle social situations and how do you keep going after all these years?"

Kathleen: "Sometimes I will have a treat at a party just to be social, but I oftentimes bring my own food. When I eat bad stuff—I feel bad afterwards. I feel great with the food I am eating, and *because I eat healthy food, I crave healthy food. We crave what we eat*. Forming good HABITS is so important. **We are our HABITS!**" We both laughed as we realized the simplicity of her statement.

Liz: "Thank you so much for sharing your health tips Kathleen, you are an inspiration to me and countless others!"

God's Medicines

Essential Oils:

Frankincense was one of the first gifts given to Jesus by the wise men. It has many healing properties. It comes from the Boswellia tree. It contains special compounds that have been found to have strong anti-inflammatory and potentially **anti-cancer effects**.

It can be mixed with a carrier oil such as coconut oil or almond oil, and can be rubbed on the skin at the site of cancer or it can be inhaled. Almost daily I rub a combination of frankincense, myrrh, lavender oil, and almond oil on my breast scars. A little bit goes a long way and it is so important to use *pure* essential oil.

Benefits of Frankincense Oil:

1. Helps reduce stress and negative emotions, without the negative side effects of a prescription drug. When inhaled it has been shown to reduce heart rate and high blood pressure and anxiety. Frankincense is known to improve memory.
2. Helps boost immune system and prevents illness.
3. Fights cancer! Do your research.
4. Heals skin and prevents signs of aging. My husband Eric applied it to a raised mole twice a day for three weeks and the mole fell off.
6. May help balance hormones and improve fertility. Used to help relieve pain, cramps, headaches, anxiety, nausea, fatigue, mood swings, arthritis, asthma and inflammation.
7. It may help regulate estrogen production reduce the risk of tumor or cyst development in premenopausal women.

8. Eases digestion. Relieves IBS, Crohn's, and Leaky Gut. When I have stomach digestive cramps, I often rub my 'go to' "frankincense lavender oil" on my belly and almost immediately my symptoms go away.

9. Acts as a sleep aid. Since it lowers anxiety and stress it can have a calming effect.

10. Frankincense is able to cross the blood-brain barrier, unlike chemotherapy chemicals. Remember, this is what the "Wise Men" gave Jesus!

Home Remedy to Help Fight Cancer:

Take 2 drops of pure (food grade) frankincense, 1 drop of myrrh and 1 drop of turmeric oil internally (in 100% juice) three times daily. Use these oils topically or diffuse them as well to fight cancer.

Sunscreen with Shea Butter and Essential Oils

My dermatologist friend revealed to me that most sunscreens have toxins that disrupt hormones and the endocrine system. Remember the skin is the largest organ of the body and it "drinks up" whatever is applied to it. You can find zinc oxide based organic sunscreen (or the ingredients to make it) online or in a health food store. Here is a DIY recipe for sunscreen:

Ingredients:
-1/2 cup Shea butter
-1/2 cup coconut oil (melted)
-15 drops carrot seed essential oil (100%)
-15 drops of myrrh essential oil (100%)

Instructions: *This sunscreen is 20 to 30 SPF:*
-Whip Shea butter until creamy. Slowly add melted coconut oil while whipping. Add essential oils and whip until fluffy. Pour into glass jar.
Tips:
-You may skip the Shea butter and just make a sunscreen oil with the above ingredients (which has an SPF of 8).
-Carrot Seed Oil has an SPF of 35.
-Myrrh Oil SPF of 15.

Healthy Lifestyle

It is important to buy foods as "organic", or at the very least, Non- GMO. Remember, if it is organic then it is automatically Non- GMO, however, if it says Non-GMO it is not necessarily organic. Finesse your budget to but Organic.

In Chris Wark's book, *Chris Beat Cancer, A Comprehensive Plan for Healing Naturally*, he talks about his diagnosis of stage 3 colon cancer, his decision to have surgery, and his decision **not** to do chemotherapy.

The oncologist told Chris he was "insane" for not doing Chemo, and most of his family did not understand. Then Chris radically changed his diet and lifestyle and is alive now nearly 16 years later! Not only does he have an excellent book but he also has an online coaching program; SQUARE ONE.

This series has some of the most informative information on cancer healing, backed by science and a "how to" program.

In *Chris Beat Cancer* he talks about the Super Health Triad:

1. Juices
2. The Giant Cancer-Fighting Salad
3. The Anti-Cancer Fruit Smoothie

I highly encourage you to get your hands on his book. Chris' anti-cancer diet is a plant-based diet. He has a ton of research to back his program.

Research: "squareone.chrisbeatcancer.com/anticancerdiet3."

In Ezekiel the Bible says:

"Their fruit will be for food and their **leaves for healing**."

The 'Forgiving' Keto Lifestyle

Eric and I eat what we call, the 'Healthy Forgiving/ Flexible Plant-Based Keto Lifestyle'.

The Ketogenic Diet was originally designed in the 1920's to help patients with epilepsy by Johns Hopkins Medical Center. A healthy Ketogenic diet should consist of about 75% Healthy fats, 20% protein and only 5% carbs (50 grams per day). The idea is to eat healthy fats, low-carb foods like eggs, nuts, fish, seeds, olive oil, avocados, coconut oil, dark chocolate, vegetables, berries, nut-butters, fermented foods, and rich cuts of meat and poultry. Stay away from processed and unhealthy/saturated fats. Eat organic when possible.

It's important not to overdo the protein! Also, limit the cheese, dairy, and red meat.

Ketosis changes the "fuel source" the body uses to stay energized: namely, from burning carbs and sugar/glucose to dietary fat. Your body is in a state of **ketosis** when your body becomes a fat burner rather than a sugar burner.

Studies show the state of ketosis starves off cancer cells.

In other words, when glucose is no longer available from food sources, we begin to burn *stored* fat instead, or fat from our food. Ketones are chemicals made in your liver that you produce when you don't have enough insulin in your body to turn sugar into energy. You need another source and so your body uses the fat instead. Then your liver changes this fat into ketones, which is a type of acid. This acid is sent into your bloodstream which begins the chemical change of ketosis.

Benefits of being in Ketosis

Studies show that being in ketosis helps with: fat loss, energy, brain fog, heart disease, cholesterol, inflammation, epilepsy, type 2 diabetes, ADD, Alzheimer's, hormones and thyroid, appetite suppression, strength, mood, sleep, digestion, skin, migraines, schizophrenia, and depression. Studies show it can **starve off cancer cells**.

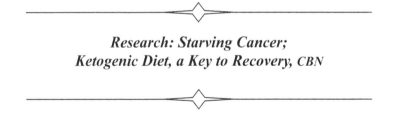

Research: Starving Cancer;
Ketogenic Diet, a Key to Recovery, CBN

Eating Ketogenic is better when done in cycles. Six days on and a day off. And remember, it is not a license to eat piles of bacon, steak, and cheese; moderation is still key!

When first starting the Keto diet, I was rather rigid about it and went through the Keto flu. This is a normal transition.

Most folks on the Keto diet, do not eat enough healthy fats and eat too much protein. After research, we stuck with it making some adjustments to our original plan. Eric and I now eat a *forgiving plant-based Keto lifestyle.* This means we allow a treat, or two, once in a while. My treat day is Sunday. I do my best to not go crazy on Sundays. 😊

I encourage folks to research the Ketogenic Diet and lifestyle before you begin the process. There are a couple of excellent videos (one is 4 minutes and the other 11 minutes) on cbn.com. Both are called Starving Cancer: Ketogenic Diet a Key to Recovery/CBN News. Also investigate *The Truth about Cancer.*

Remember, God says:

"My people perish for lack of knowledge."

Tips from a Nutritional Oncologist:

Remember my friend Rose? The one who had the single mastectomy? Well, her Nutritional Oncologist gave her a complete Action Plan following surgery, and the insurance even covered the appointments. The Nutritional M.D. had previously become disillusioned in the *traditional medical community* and decided to change her focus to a more holistic approach.

Now we can all benefit from her change of heart and great knowledge. The following recommendations may help change the terrain within our bodies creating a hostile environment for cancer. Note: it is likely that we all have a few rogue cancer cells floating around our body.

Lifestyle Recommendations- Nutritional Oncologist:

- Try to maintain a healthy weight
- 8-10 servings of organic fruits and vegetables a day
- Avoid sugary drinks
- Exercise 6 days a week for at least 30 minutes
- Intermittent Fasting Everyday: eating only between 12 noon and 8 at night ideally fasting for 13 to 16 hours. When the body is deprived of food it kicks into ketosis. Drinking water, coffee, or tea is fine, ideally no sweetened drinks during the fasting time. Not too much coffee or it turns our stomach into a 'pool of acid!'
- **Water**: 6-8 glasses of **DISTILLED, Purified, or Spring** water a day. Take a multivitamin with minerals since the filtration removes some of the important minerals. Use glass or BPA-free bottles.
- Limited beverages during a meal (even a half hour before and after) because it washes away the digestive acids and enzymes.

Daily Supplement Recommendations- Nutritional Oncologist:

- Fish Oil Capsules – Mercury Free, with high EPA
- Curcumin (concentrated turmeric root)
- A good multivitamin (Garden of Life)
- Probiotics
- Vitamin D

- CoQ10 with ubiquinol
- Vitamin E with Selenium
- Vitamin C
- Green Tea Capsule
- Magnesium/Calcium (2 parts Mag. to 1 Cal.)

Recommended Foods- Nutritional Oncologist:
- Nuts (walnuts are a super cancer fighter) and seeds
- Olives, Cucumbers, and Pickles
- Berry/ veggie smoothies with organic protein powder
- Organic berries are the best fruit because they contain compounds that are anti-cancer, anti-oxidant, and anti-inflammatory. Watermelon.
- Elderberry –helps beat the flu, colds and strengthens immunity. The University of Maryland Medical Center concluded that: "Elder(berry) may have anti-inflammatory, antiviral, and anticancer properties."
- Organic eggs (preferably Omega 3's)
- Bone Broth
- Cruciferous vegetables – broccoli, broccolini, cauliflower, brussel sprouts, cabbage, bok choy, broccoli sprouts,
- Dark Leafy Greens – spinach, collards, kale, spring mix, romaine (contains folic acid)
- Avocados
- Orange foods (contain carotenes): sweet potato, carrots, beets, tomatoes, squash, and pumpkin
- Celery and red pepper - (prevents cancer)
- Garlic, onions, beets, radishes

- Organic Herbs: parsley and cilantro are particularly effective detoxifiers
- Extra virgin olive oil/anti-inflammatory (do not heat past smoking point or it can turn carcinogenic), Avocado and grape seed oil, and Coconut Oil are also good for cooking and dressings
- Kombucha, kimchi, sauerkraut
- Mushrooms – enhance immune system and best if cooked. Mushroom supplements are effective too.
- Citrus fruits & apples in moderation due to the sugar
- Green tea/organic (several glasses a day with a little lemon and honey – served cold or hot)
- Ginger tea – can help to dissolve kidney stones, cleanse liver, and fight cancer cells.
- Legumes: contain fiber, decreases inflammation
- Bitter Raw Apricot seeds – a natural antioxidant that may help fight cancer.
- Lemons – all parts can help fight cancer and strengthen the immune system. Lemon peel impedes tumor growth according to recent studies.

Liz's Suggested Bonus Foods (all organic, of course!)
- Hummus and Pesto
- Almond Butter
- Dark Chocolate (65% or darker)
- Honey (Moderation)
- Maple Syrup (Moderation)
- Marinated Artichoke Hearts
- Guacamole and Salsa

- Organic Mayonnaise, mustard, relish, Chow Chow.
- Chicken Apple Sausage or Turkey Bacon
- Balsamic Vinaigrette
- Organic Soups
- Perrier Water
- Goat Cheese
- Grapefruit and Bananas
- Frozen "riced" cauliflower
- Wild caught Salmon, Tuna, or Mahi Mahi
- Chicken Thighs and Grass Fed Beef
- As a treat organic popcorn, tortilla chips, or whole grain bread (Ezekiel or Dave's Killer Bread)

The Candida Culprit and Cure

One day while at a health food store, an associate helping us explained, "***Candida is a culprit in many cancers.***" Many studies show there is Candida fungus in cancer cells. She told us about a customer whose husband had stage four melanoma. After a mole was surgically removed, he did a major Candida cleanse followed by a diet of no sugar, no dairy, no gluten and no chemotherapy and ***when they tested him for cancer it was completely gone!***

The store clerk emphasized low sugar, low carbs and dairy. She recommended apricot kernels, a healthy gut, probiotics and baking soda daily. "Candida causes inflammation in the body and inflammation causes disease." Then with passion she said: "Get ahead of the situation before it starts to grow!" She smiled and waved at us as we left the store with a bag of vitamins, ground flax seed, apricot kernels, aloe vera juice.

Causes for Candida overgrowth in the body include: antibiotics, birth control pills, and excessive sugar.

Natural Remedies to fight off Candida:

- Baking Soda, 1 tsp in a glass of water, daily.
- Aloe Vera Juice 100%
- Probiotics, acidophilus, multi-vitamins, flaxseed, garlic.
- Veggies, fish, brown rice, millet, fermented foods, gluten free grains, bone broth.
- Plain yogurt (Greek – *with full fat* 4-5%)
- Drink alkaline or distilled water.
- Cranberry juice or capsules (100%)
- Scrape your tongue with a spoon to get off any white sludge slime.
- Change toothbrush once a month or run it under boiling hot water.
- Essential Oils: clove, oregano, cinnamon, grapefruit.
- Candida Cleanse: Add 1 drop of clove oil to a smoothie for two weeks.

    Avoid: Fruit, sugar, yeast, carbs (bread, buns, chips) dry fruits, aged cheese, grains, nut- butter, potatoes, citrus, tomatoes, pineapple.

I know the above suggestions seem pretty extreme, but if you have a *yeast infection or cancer*, you will do ANYTHING! Apparently if the body is Keto and 'Alkaline' it starves 'Candida'. Alkalinity test strips are available to test your urine.

Constipation and Gut Health

I believe that my colon cancer was caused in great part due to CONSTIPATION! The food was festering in my colon for days at a time!!!

Eric and I now make a drink every morning with:
1 Tbsp of Apple Cider Vinegar, 2 Tbsp of *Ground Flaxseed*, ¼ cup Aloe Vera Juice, warm water, Elderberry syrup or Kombucha and lemon... and I have been *regular* ever since!

Main causes of slow digestion are lack of: water, healthy fats, Probiotics, and fiber in the diet. Stress, inactivity, certain medications, and magnesium deficiency.

Lifestyle choices are key: move more, drink more fluids, eat clean and take the right supplements, including peppermint, 100% Aloe Vera Juice, ginger, magnesium, Probiotics, and **ground flax seeds. Flax seed changed my life!** Also, coconut milk powder is excellent on the intestines and helps greatly with IBS. I put a tablespoon in my *half-caff* coffee every morning.

Research shows that 80% of our overall health is determined by our *Gut Health*. Probiotics, fiber and fermented foods are critical. Try to avoid antibiotics because they wipe out the good bacteria.

Ask yourself:
"Did God make this or did *man* make this?"

The Cleveland Clinic's Dr. Mark Hyman, author of an excellent book, *Food: What the Heck Should I Eat?* says, "It's really simple: Ask yourself, *'Did God make this or did man make this?'* Did God make a Twinkie? No. Did God make an Avocado? Yes."

When we bring God into the picture with our healthy food choices, it changes everything. Are we willing to do it?

My Prayer: *"Dear Generous Father in Heaven, thank You for being so patient with me, your often stubborn, disobedient child. Over and over You have tried to get my attention and prompt me to change my ways. I am so sorry for being so rebellious. It took me 3 cancers before I was willing to make 'Big Changes' with food and lifestyle. Thank You for waking me up! I vow to buy healthy food for me and my family and do my best to care for my body, Your temple. Please help me! I love You."*

Love Your Contrite Daughter, Liz

Your Prayer and Reflection: What can you buy differently at the grocery store and how can you re-stock your shelves and feed your family with 'God's Food' and not man's food?

_____

_____

_____

The Devil's Food

And Other Evils

"Do not desire his delicacies, for they are deceptive food."
— Proverbs 23:3

I awoke at 3 a.m. with a stabbing pain in my stomach. I hobbled downstairs to get a glass of warm milk. Reaching for the refrigerator door, the pain overtook me. I called out to my husband, "Honey, I need you!"

Immediately, I clutched my stomach, dropped to the hardwood floor, and blacked out. *Quite literally, I was floored*. I slipped into an altered state, where a spiritual warfare raged. Demonic type voices were shrieking. The screaming in my head was relentless.

Two demons were screeching at each other, hovering around my head. There were teeth gnashing and hissing, even spitting:

"We must leave now! She is not a good host for us!"

The shrill voices continued while noisy cymbals clanged in my ears, the demons barked;

"She will become a warrior for God if we leave!"

"No!! We must go now!!"

The voices were oppressing me, hammering my head. It felt violent. There were flashing strobe lights. It seemed like what hell might be like, and it was right in my face. Then, finally, there was dead silence.

I lay limp, almost lifeless. Slowly my consciousness returned. The voices in my head were gone; I came back to my sweet husband, back to the world. I opened my eyes, and wondered who I was and where I was.

Eric was cradling me on the floor, and he was praying fervently over me. My husband thought he was losing me, his new bride, as my eyes had rolled back into my head and he had given me mouth-to-mouth resuscitation during the surreal episode.

As I lay like a large wet noodle in Eric's arms, I felt my body convulse one last time. I rolled over and purged every last impurity out of my body. I vomited, cried huge cleansing tears, and peed. My nose dripped. I purged, and I purged good. Every orifice of my body spit out the devil and his evil demon henchmen.

My precious Eric cleaned me up, wiped off the floor and carried me back to our bedroom. At sunrise, I awoke tender, tired, and with a softer heart. I felt like a newborn baby. And in that moment when my eyes opened, I knew I would not drink alcohol again.

That morning, while still lying in bed, Eric and I looked at each other with awe and a bit of confusion. We wanted to make sense of what had happened the night before. The only explanation that we came up with was that God heard our prayers and purged a demon, or two. This makes absolute sense as we had prayed the prayer to: "*Cast out and away any demons from us, bind them up, cast them away, and pour the healing loving blood of Jesus over us*," for months.

We know that God answers prayers, and that prayers are powerful and effective. Eric and I believe the Holy Spirit had done a mighty work as a response to our prayer. The alcohol stronghold on me was removed, and the chain of bondage was broken.

My alcohol issue had followed me for years. *I had lost a baby, a marriage, twelve inches of my intestines, and had a dream from God "Do not drink wine," but it would take me being sprawled out on the floor half dead, to wake me up.*

After my deliverance from alcohol, Eric gave it up too. He knew it would be a stumbling block for me if he kept drinking. He admitted to issues with drinking over the years. Eric believed that I was "interceding," or taking the "hit" for him too through this trial I endured on the floor. He said he wanted to give it up for God first and foremost.

Dramatically the desire for drinking was taken completely away from us. We give God the glory. This would add to our testimony for God—not to mention the health and spiritual benefits. In my life, I had been drinking on and off for over 30 years; mostly on.

Since the episode, in November of 2008 we have not consumed alcohol, nor do we have it in our home. I have had very little desire for wine or other alcohol. No more dry mouth, no more puffiness or headaches in the morning. Eric's chronic stomach pains have disappeared completely.

As Eric says, "We never need a designated driver!"

After our dramatic night on the floor, Eric and I made a pact to break the generational curse of alcohol dependency in our own family. *It would start with us.*

As you read the following sections please keep an open heart as this is what we have researched and discovered after our war-faring encounter.

Alcohol America

Jesus First Strategy:
"Be sober-minded and do not be drunk on wine... be filled with the Spirit."

Satan has a stronghold on most of America. Much new research shows that beer, wine and alcohol have a strong correlation to cancer. Especially to breast, colon and intestinal cancers.

In my own experience, I found it difficult to have the recommended one glass a day. It usually turned into more; two, three, or four. Studies show that alcohol causes a loss of sex drive and erectile dysfunction, depression, anxiety, weight gain, car accidents, death, divorce, diabetes, pickled liver, alcohol dementia, among other spiritual and physical ills.

When married people have been drinking, they sometimes forget they are married. It also can cause restless sleep. After the alcohol sugar wears off, the body goes through withdrawals one often awakes abruptly during sleep.

Alcohol can cause birth defects within the first few weeks of pregnancy and often people are drunk when they have sex, out of marriage, resulting in guilt, anxiety and sometimes an unwanted pregnancy.

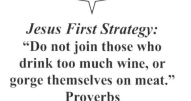

Jesus First Strategy:
"Do not join those who drink too much wine, or gorge themselves on meat."
Proverbs

Often sexual abuse occurs when the perpetrator has been drinking. Alcohol is

technically a depressant. After the initial high the low sets in. *The higher one gets at night the lower one feels in the morning.*

God's Word instructs us:

"Be sober-minded; be watchful. Your adversary the devil prowls around like a roaring lion, seeking someone to devour." (1Peter 5:8)

But what about the benefits of wine, people mention?
The same heart benefits can be found in the supplement, Resveratrol. Some justify drinking with: "Jesus turned water into wine." But in Biblical days, wine disinfected the water

and contained a much lower content of alcohol. God says: *"Do not get drunk on wine; be filled with the Spirit"* (Eph 5:18).

Is Gluttony a Sin?

Are we not called to take care of our bodies; these *Temples of God?*

I recently read: "Satan has a stronghold on America with sugar, alcohol, illegal drugs, prescription drugs, soda, pig, shellfish, carbs and gluttony."

My husband once said, "Gluttony is the *hidden sin in plain sight.* There are so many 'stalwart' believers out there who struggle with that final sin."

Many people do not think eating to excess is a sin; however the Bible refers to gluttony 36 times. Scripture condemns excessive greed for food, unrestrained self-indulgence and a rejection of Godly moderation. Even though I'm fairly trim, it is one of my biggest struggles in life—eating moderately.

Obesity is often the sin that many Christians find easy to laugh about and accept as harmless. It is the sin believers like to ignore; accepted and tolerate. The "Pot" luck shows around our waist. It is no laughing matter.

Proverbs says, *"Do not join those who drink too much wine, or gorge themselves on meat."*

Philippians 3:19 warns: *"Whose end is destruction and whose god is their belly."* Overeating is simply another form of Idolatry. Remember, Esau sold his birthright for food!

Why not substitute Toxic Processed desserts, white rolls and prepackaged potato salad *with* the healthier options such as *angel* eggs, veggies and hummus, tuna salad, frittata, chicken salad, Cobb Salad, keto chili, grilled chicken, green salad, healthy spaghetti, healthy banana bread, fruit salad, broccoli salad, veggie wraps, coleslaw, , guacamole, near Keto peanut butter balls, near keto granola, Healthy Brownies, or Healthy Peach Crisp!? (see recipes at the end of the book).

Some research shows that cancer cannot survive in an **alkaline** environment. Our American eating habits tend toward acid forming foods. The foods themselves may be acidic or alkaline, but it is how our body reacts to the food that is the key. For example, apple cider vinegar is acidic so our body responds with forming alkalinity overpowering the acid. As discussed earlier, **Candida** is another culprit causing vaginal yeast infections, canker sores, and possibly cancer. If our bodies are Alkaline, Candida shrinks away. Win/Win.

The enemy wants us addicted to sugar and carbs, causing disease and shorting lives. Why? So we won't be healthy and alive to share the Good News and Glorify God. Could our testimony to non-believers be weakened if we have lack of self-control and are overweight?

Someone once told me "Christian love desires what is best for oneself or another." We must encourage each other to eat healthy, resisting the devil. Satan wants us to eat bad food, drinks and drugs instead of healthy food and Jesus.

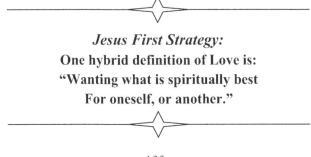

Jesus First Strategy:
One hybrid definition of Love is:
"Wanting what is spiritually best
For oneself, or another."

Milk and Dairy Woes

Recently at the store, as I was checking out, I was chatting with the cashier. I mentioned being six years cancer free.

She asked, "Did you know it's not good to drink milk because it feeds cancer. My friend who had cancer told me about this connection."

I said, "oh, what about cheese?"

She said, "Goat cheese and feta cheese are okay." Then she went on to tell me about a goat farm down the road.

As we were driving home from Lowes, I looked up milk and dairy on my phone and it turns out milk has 4 million parts of puss per teaspoon! It also can cause mucous in the body resulting in Candida, coughing and other ills.

I also learned that dairy can add estrogen to the body and fat cells that can contribute to estrogen fed cancer. My heart skipped a beat because my breast cancer from several years ago was estrogen fed cancer. I had a decision to make. How was I going to take care of my body going forward? Would I transition from cow to goat's milk and cheese?

Our son Nolan once said to me "Why would we drink milk from cows—we are humans!"

Since then I have learned that we are the only mammals that drink milk after we have been weaned off our mothers. At midlife, many people develop lactose intolerance. This is tough since we all love cheese.

After my encounter in Lowes, I've been slowly changing over from cow's milks to coconut milk, almond milk and occasionally will splurge with organic ice cream or organic milk on Keto granola. We now love goat cheese.

Dr. Mercola's List of Foods *Banned* in Other Countries:

- **Milk and Dairy** Products laced with rBGH (growth hormones which can cause early menstruation) Look for products labeled as "rBGH-free".
- **Non grass-fed meat** (if it is not grass fed they are pumped full of chemicals to make them plumper).
- **Mountain Dew** – contains a chemical flame retardant.
- **Processed foods with artificial food colors** and dyes for example: boxed mac & cheese, Jell-O and many kids' cereals (can cause behavior problems as well as cancer).
- **Chicken that is not organic**-- is likely injected with hormones and arsenic based drugs.
- **Bread with Potassium Bromate** – this is white bread. Recommend organic, whole grain bread.
- **Olestra/Olean** – is a "fake fat" found in potato chips & french-fries, causing leaky gut, diarrhea, and weight gain.
- **Preservatives BHA and BHT** - found in breakfast cereals, dehydrated potatoes and beer. Linked to cancer...
- **Farm – Raised Salmon** – steer clear of all farmed fish – do your best to buy wild caught fish.
- **Contaminated drinking water**

Remember, the devil, satan (with a little "d & s") has been referred to as "The ruler of the air." Satan came to *steal, kill and destroy. He hates us*, and wants us dead and in Hell. Thankfully, "Jesus came to give us life in abundance, and He overcame the world!"

Don't throw in the Towel

It seems like everything causes cancer these days. The food we eat, the air we breathe, the water we drink, the thoughts we think. And 'Organics are too expensive'. It's easy to just throw in the towel and give up and not do anything to improve our odds for health. That attitude is a 'Cop-Out'.
I recently saw a show on how to stay healthy in a toxic world.

The take home message was: we can't avoid every toxic lotion, carcinogenic food, or drink; however, if we can do **80% healthy and 20% not so healthy,** we have the odds in our favor. Our bodies are very resilient and can fight off a lot of toxic chemicals and pollutants; however, they can reach a breaking point. As stewards of our body, we are called to do what we can to be healthy.

Please refer to Chapter 18 for more information of things to reduce or eliminate.

What is Pharmakeia?

Strong's Concordance 5331, defines *Pharmakeia*: "As the use of medicine, drugs or spells."

It's interesting that the New Testament Greek word translated "sorcery" or "witchcraft" is *pharmakeia*, which is the source of our English word pharmacy. In Paul's day, the word primarily meant "dealing in poison" or "drug use" and was applied to divination and spell casting because sorcerers often used drugs along with their incantations to conjure up occultic power.

Are We a Pharmakeia Nation?

"For by your Sorcery (pharmakeia) all the nations were deceived." (Revelation 18:23b)

*A*nn was 7 years old as she sat on her Granddaddy's lap in 1950. He told her two prophetic messages:

"Annie, the Bible says that your generation will see the return of Jesus..." then with shocking revelation, he said: "America will be destroyed. Not from the outside, but from within—with Drugs."

Annie recently shared this story with me on a walk together one morning. It made me pause. I thought of what may be coming. And I thought of my own childhood.

Growing up in Santa Barbara, in a family of 5, with my Dad as a doctor, I learned a lot. Whenever I was sick or sore, it seemed Dad's remedy was water. I never saw a Pediatrician.

"Soak the splinter in warm water," Dad would say. Or, "Drink lots of water and put your head over a bowl of steamy water and take a hot shower." Or my favorite still today, "Put a hot water bottle on your sore tummy."

Dad's remedies were usually natural, inexpensive and easy. Most often they involved water and the *tincture of time*. In fact, this water remedy concept has intrigued so many people, my Dad, my husband and I have compiled a book called, **The Water Doctor**. There are over 40 natural remedies. While water may be God's all-time best remedy, mankind often gets into trouble when *we* play God.

A pastor friend defined *Pharmakeia* as:

"Wanting the healing, without repentance."

My husband, Eric, says, "If a check engine light lights up on your car dashboard, you have two options; you can fix the engine or cut the wire to the dashboard.

Taking pharmaceuticals is like cutting the wire. The root problem still exists—it may ease a few symptoms, but will not solve the underlying issues."

Top Pharmaceutical Side Effects:

- **Weight Gain**
- **Depression**
- **Low Sex Drive**
- **Bursts of Anger**
- **Cancer**

Have you ever noticed that the pharmaceutical drug symbol is a long staff with two snakes encircling the rod? Very interesting that the symbol of the devil is also a snake.

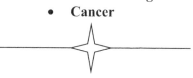

Sorcery is an attempt to bypass God's wisdom and power. God calls it an "Abomination." It is the easy way out. The pills and potions are often created in "darkness." The spiritual battle is real so please bathe every drug decision in **prayer**.

Turning to God or Man?

We could always spot one older relative in church if we came in late; we just searched for her "bobbing" white – haired head. She was taking twelve pharmaceutical drugs prescribed by doctors. After her family looked over all her bottles of pills, they took them into her doctor asking, "Which ones are absolutely necessary?"

Slowly, my dear relative weaned off of several medications. At 95 years old her head is now steady as she sits in the pew at church.

A startling statistic; Prescription Drug Reactions are now the <u>fourth</u> leading cause of death in the United States! Source: U.S. News/Health

Are we choosing drugs and pharmaceuticals over God's wisdom, power, and natural remedies? Do we embrace drugs instead of self-control? Self-control seems to be the hardest fruit to bear. It comes down to sin. In Galatians 5 it says, *"Now the works of the flesh are evident: sexual immorality, impurity, sensuality, idolatry, sorcery... drunkenness, orgies, and things like these. I warn you... those who do such things will **not inherit** the kingdom of God."*

What about the COVID Cure?

God warns against sorcery and witchcraft throughout the Bible and as believers, we are to avoid a life of relying on "pharma". In this day of "panic over pandemics," we are called to be the voice of reason. We must turn to God first.

An un-Godly world will desire scientific answers, such as vaccines over God's true medicine. According to many of America's faithful *Frontline Physicians*, the Covid Vaccine is RNA replicating, using tracking isotopes. It may change human DNA permanently. Our genome may become "part human and part Artificial Intelligence." Is this the "Mark of the Beast," spoken of in Revelation 13? Will we need it to buy, sell or travel, or even go out into public?

My father, the Endocrinologist, M.D., says that a virus, such as Covid 19, mutates too quickly for a vaccine to work. Flu shots are effective for just 1 in 100 strains, during a seasonal flu.

Our Heavenly Father, however, created natural remedies, healthy immune boosting foods, oils and wholesome lifestyles to keep disease at bay and heal sicknesses. The best way to combat and prevent COVID is with Vitamin C, Sunshine, Vitamin D, Zinc, and Rest.

In Biblical days there were "holistic" doctors. The implication is that they used prayer, fasting and natural herbs and essential oils for healings, as opposed to man-made potions. A friend recently sent me this information,

"Jesus called Luke out of his profession as a doctor to walk as an apostle, healing by the power of God not by what he learned in school/practice." When God directed me to use a naturopath doctor it was a true blessing. He gave advice that would not be dispensed by standard medical doctors in America. His advice contributed toward my healing.

My brother, who is a Dermatologist, said the majority of his patients expect a prescription before leaving his office. Many times we prefer a "quick fix," or pill, rather than doing the work. Maybe that is human nature. Researchers from *the Mayo Clinic found,* **"Nearly 70% of Americans are on one or more prescription drugs."** How many more are on illegal drugs?

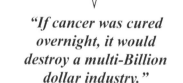

"If cancer was cured overnight, it would destroy a multi-Billion dollar industry."
-Pastor Tate -

My husband says, **"Pharmaceutical companies rarely create cures, they create customers."**

Let us be wise. God's Word says, *"Cursed are those who put their trust in mere humans."* (Jeremiah 17:5).

It is interesting to note that in Nazi Germany, Hitler provided Dexedrine (Speed) to his entire army; it caused them to be aggressive, fear-based and controllable, like robots. They killed millions of innocent people.

Chris Wark, in his book, *Chris Beat Cancer* reveals, "Every year over 127,000 people taking the prescribed doses are dying from reactions to those drugs." Three of the biggest overlooked side effects of pharmaceuticals are weight gain, reduced sex drive and cancer. It's hard to imagine a tiny white pill has such a huge effect on the body.

One Pastor said, "Both legal and illegal drugs can allow an opening for demons to afflict people."

The Multibillion Dollar Industry

There are a lot of good caring doctors out there; they are just 'trapped in a bad system'. Some doctors over-prescribe medications, because of a fear of law suits.

A pastor friend recently shared, "If cancer was cured overnight, it would destroy a multi-billion-dollar industry."

Doctors have helped me over the years with surgeries, and some good advice. Unfortunately, some of those surgeries and drugs caused new problems. Abdominal scar tissue led to more surgeries. The estrogen-based birth-control pills and the annual mammograms/radiation likely contributed to my breast cancer.

141

Before Taking Chemotherapy Please Consider:

One study revealed that the average cancer patient brings in over $300,000.00 in revenue to the medical system. We know dozens upon dozens of people who refused chemotherapy and drastically changed their lifestyle. They are alive and thriving today.

A friend of ours who trained oncologists, with chemotherapy use, said, "Chemotherapy is such a strong chemical that it kills both the good and bad cells. It can lead to hair loss, major nausea, and permanent cell damage. And after remission the cancer can re-surface." At dinner one night, she discussed leaving her job due to the guilt. "I train doctors in dispensing chemo, bug poison." After a long pause, she continued, *"Did you know when some types of chemotherapy are dropped onto a concrete floor; it will burn a hole in the concrete?"*

In fact, *a main ingredient in many chemotherapy drugs is mustard gas,* which was used in WWI as chemical warfare. Now it's a cancer cure? *The Journal of Clinical Oncology* did a massive study on chemo results. Chemo is beneficial in just 2.3% of cases. It was destructive in the remaining 97.7% of cases. The brain is often permanently damaged.

In *Chris Beat Cancer,* it says, "Chemo-therapy literally means 'treating disease with chemicals.'"

"The pharmaceutical/chemo lobby is possibly the most powerful lobby in the world," according to one legislator. Members of Congress *have received hundreds of thousands of dollars in donations,* according to Forbes.

Today, each pharmaceutical company is known for their particular pills or medications. They promote through TV commercials, doctors and magazine advertisements. Pharmaceutical companies seem to do whatever it takes to control government regulations and push their products, even though they often have horrible side effects.

Praying for Wisdom and Health

We must be very discerning, pray, and take time to decide what treatments to use. Then prayerfully consider what physicians or naturopath doctors to consult, if any. When we hear guidance from God, it will line up with scripture.

After each of my 3 cancers diagnosis, I prayed for God's guidance and felt called to do surgery to remove the unhealthy tissue. I am grateful for those awesome surgeons. One friend mentioned that surgery is okay because it's in the Bible. I felt led *not* to do chemo, radiation, or any pharmaceutical drugs, but rely on God's Word and God's Food. I am grateful to God for my many healings several years ago. Each of us must work out "our own salvation with fear and trembling." I pray that God reveals to you the best plan for your healing or continued health.

How do we decide when to take pharmaceuticals, get surgery, and consult physicians/naturopathic doctors?
1. Is our doctor or naturopath doctor a follower of Jesus, or willing to pray with us for God's guidance?
2. Are the recommended Pharmaceutical drugs *altered by man* (for profit)? Or are they natural from the earth?
3. Would repentance of a behavior help me recover without drugs or surgery? (i.e. change our diet, lifestyle or thinking)

4. Is it a ***long-term or temporary drug?*** Is it addictive?
5. Have I received more than one opinion?
6. Have I prayed about the situation, and searched the Bible?

One more important point, Dear Reader:

Please let this book be a warning to you and your loved ones. It is the "call" of every believer to warn others of evils, otherwise "the blood will be on our hands," according to Ezekiel 32:21. I beg you to pass this information on.

My Prayer: *"Dear God, our Great Physician, Forgive us for ingesting toxins and manmade junk. We repent. Help me to make healthy choices for myself and my family. Forgive us for turning to pharma drugs, illegal drugs, doctors, and alcohol and food, rather than You. Bind up the evil and greed in the drug and alcohol industries and release Your ministering angels" Love Your Daughter, Liz*

Your Prayer and Reflection: What unhealthy foods or drinks can you delete or decrease in your life? How can you trust God over drugs and pharma in your life?

_____

_____

_____

Sugar Feeds Cancer

"Have you found honey –sugar-? Eat only as much as you need lest you be filled with it and vomit."— Proverbs 25:16

*I*t was the day after Thanksgiving. Upon awaking, I sensed a calling to *fast* for the day for my friend Grace. She was recovering from brain cancer surgery. I had seen many miracles from fasting; it was the least I could do for my sister in Christ.

As I entered our colorful kitchen, I conveniently forgot the plan, and sliced myself a big chunk of Turkey Day pumpkin pie. I topped it with whipped cream and poured myself a cup of Eric's fresh ground coffee. Sometimes, I justify the splurge with the reassurance that the treats are homemade; Pie sweetened only with maple syrup. More treats beckoned.

A nice lunch followed, with maple syrup chocolate fudge brownies, and several dark-chocolate covered pretzels.

After dinner, another big chunk of pumpkin pie mounded with whipped cream slips into my mouth. As I lay tossing and turning in bed that night, there was heartburn in my chest. Slowly, I headed downstairs for natural remedy, to quench the fire in my esophagus. I didn't make it very far.

Suddenly, I felt dizzy and faint and I called upstairs to Eric, "Honey." No answer. "Sweetie!" No answer. As I lay on the floor with my head spinning, I mustered all of my strength calling out one last time, "Sweetie!"

Eric came sleepily down the stairs then stepped into action when he saw me on the floor. "What happened?" he wondered.

I said weakly, "I think it's a Sugar Demon...." Then in desperation I managed two more words before blacking out, "please pray!"

The next few minutes felt like an eternity, tumbling head-first down a steep hill. Bump, bump, bang... I hit bottom.

Slowly I came back to the world and my husband.

Eric was praying with great authority as he gently held my shoulders, "In the name of Jesus Christ of Nazareth, demons leave my wife! Lord, I cast any sugar demons away in the name of Jesus, and pour the healing loving blood of Jesus over her....in Jesus name I pray..."

I began to weep, "Oh, sweetie, I have been fighting with the sugar demons since I was a little girl." Suddenly, I felt the stronghold lift. God had removed these bantering demons that cajoled me to binge every Sunday for so many years.

Sugar Addictions

The devil has a stronghold on most of America. It is called sugar addiction. Studies show that sugar is more addictive than cocaine and it is wreaking havoc on our health. Cocaine and sugar both interact with the brain's reward system.

Research has shown that more than 82% of Americans exceed the recommended sugar intake. In fact, the "Sugar Film" documentary reveals that most Americans consume 40 teaspoons of sugar per day.

One hundred years ago we consumed an average of 2 pounds of sugar per year and guess how much we consume now? We now average 152 pounds of sugar consumption per year. *I am so shocked, as I am sure you are, that I am going to repeat that...As Americans, we used to eat 2 pounds of sugar per year, and now we consume 152 pounds per year on average.* This is equal to three pounds or six cups of sugar consumed each week.

The maximum daily amount of recommended sugar in calories and teaspoons (tsp):

For Men: 150 calories per day or 36 grams (9 tsp).

For Women: 100 calories per day or 24 grams (6 tsp).

Our beverages are a big contributor to our sugar intake. One 12-ounce can of Coke has 10 teaspoons, or 39 grams of sugar. A 20-ounce bottle of Pepsi has 13.8 teaspoons of sugar; that is a whopping 69 grams of sugar!

Ounce for ounce, orange juice and apple juice contain the same amount of sugar as a can of coke, 39 grams, or 10 teaspoons! But a small orange has only 14 grams of sugar.

New research shows that artificial sweeteners are just as harmful and cancer causing as regular sweeteners.

Two large glasses of sweet white wine contain 30 grams of sugar. That is over the maximum recommended amount of sugar for a woman for an entire day. We get sugar in almost every food that is pre-packaged or processed. Fast-food is packed with sugar and other addictive toxic ingredients. Additionally, carbs like pasta, white bread, white rice, and chips all turn into sugar once they reach our stomach. Ugh.

Cancer

So if sugar feeds cancer, no wonder cancer is running wild. Many studies show that everyone has a few cancerous cells floating around in their bodies. Thankfully our immune systems hold most of them at bay. Cancer refers to uncontrolled cell division or abnormal cell growth.

"Cancer lights up in a PET Scan, when sugar water is injected…"

We must be prudent and wake up to the fact that the food industry packs sugar into almost all prepackaged, processed foods. They have so many names and aliases for sugar: Fructose, Dextrose, Glucose, Sucrose, Fructose syrup, High Fructose corn syrup, Corn syrup, Beet sugar, Agave, Cane sugar, Brown sugar, Corn syrup solids, Evaporated cane juice, Galactose. Read the labels on your food, watch for words ending in "ose" or "syrup".

A jarring fact is that cancer lights up in a PET Scan after glucose is injected into the body. Glucose or sugar-water is cancer's favorite food. In fact sugar and carbs (that turn to sugar) fertilize cancer. The sugar accumulates around the cancerous tumors, and is like a light bulb on the scan.

Some complex carbs may be okay (whole wheat and whole grains) but to starve off the cancer cells a strict Plant based Keto diet may be in order: rich in healthy fats, some protein, lots of veggies, nuts and some berries. Do your homework.

Diabetes

I recently received a prayer chain request from a friend in California. The request said, "Please pray for Glenda as she prepares for a leg amputation. This is her second leg amputation and the surgery will remove her leg from her knee down. Please pray for her husband John as he assists her through this difficult surgery."

I knew Glenda quite well when we lived in California. I knew that she was diabetic and struggled with alcohol (which is packed with sugar). She also loved her sweets and carbs at the potlucks. Glenda's not the first one I know who had her limbs removed as a result of diabetes. I have another friend, Lisa, who had one foot and one leg removed as a result of the limb dying off from diabetes; She died shortly after.

I also have a couple of friends who have been able to *reverse* their diabetes by going on the Keto/ plant-based diet or drastically changing their diet by limiting carbs and sugar.

There was a comedian on America's Got Talent recently.

Her big joke was:

"I tried a new diet; it was a healthy blender drink diet. I made one with kale, spinach, broccoli, and celery... it tasted so bad I decided I would rather be diabetic." (notice "die" is in the word when pronouncing "diabetic").

Spiritual Battle

After my episode on the floor fighting the sugar demons that had been oppressing me for years, I realized there is more than just a physical component to the addiction. It also has a spiritual element. A demonic element. Why is it that 71% of adults are either obese or overweight? Do people lack will power? Do we eat mostly prepackaged processed foods filled with carbs and sugar and drink too much soda, or diet soda? How about fast food? Too many sugar packed coffee drinks? What about alcohol? It's loaded with sugar.

Maybe we need a nationwide cleansing. A sugar detox. And a processed food detox. Maybe an alcohol and carb detox; And dairy too. And yes, it takes more time to cook meals from scratch, and yes, it is a bit more expensive to buy organic fruits, vegetables and nuts, eggs and fish, but if our very lives depend on it would we do it?

It took me three cancers before I was willing to make big changes to my Standard American Diet (SAD).

Please learn from me. Cancer is horrible! Just miserable!

But take heart, healthy eating can be delicious and healing at the same time. It is a journey, a process if you will, to change the food in our kitchen and in our recipes.

Did you know man invented refined sugar? – God invented honey, maple syrup, the stevia plant and more. In the Bible days, they did not eat sugar. It was not yet invented by man. But Jesus and His disciples had a delicious diet without white sugar.

What did Jesus eat? Fifteen Super Foods!
1. Fish
2. Bread (with wheat, barley, legumes and olive oil)
3. Pistachios
4. Walnuts
5. Almonds
6. Garlic
7. Cumin
8. Mustard
9. Cucumbers
10. Frankincense
11. Legumes
12. Olives
13. Pomegranates
14. Figs
15. Dates

Here's one definition of addiction:
"Addiction = continuing with a behavior, even though it has negative consequences."

Tips to Break the Sugar Habit

Sugar cravings run in my family. When I was in High School, I was barely chubby, but my Mom wanted me to attend *Overeaters Anonymous* with her. I will never forget sitting at the big conference table with twenty or so overweight people. At the start of the meetings, each person gave their "Confessional Statement." One at a time we went around the circle saying:

"Hi my name is _____ and I am a compulsive over-eater." They even assigned me a "Sponsor," like in Alcoholics Anonymous!

I remember calling my sponsor one day when I was ready to eat an entire frozen sheet-cake, "Help! I'm going on a binge!" She helped me consider my feelings and cravings. I had secretly been sneaking treats after school for years.

"Can you make an agreement with me now, that you will take a walk or bike ride, until the craving passes?" It worked.

Recently, one of my adult daughters shared that she struggles with sugar and food like I do. Thankfully, she gave me a few tricks that she learned, so here they are:

First, be aware if you are "eating your feelings." Do I eat when I am angry, lonely, sad, tired, or feeling down? Does food comfort me when I have those feelings? Awareness is half the battle. Be prepared when those feelings strike.

Most crimes are crimes of opportunity and most eating is out of opportunity or convenience. It helps to eat a snack before grocery shopping, dining out or heading to a party. And don't buy processed foods. If you buy treats, freeze them in single portion sizes and only pull out one at a time.

Consider doing a family detox from sugar, carbs, dairy, and alcohol. It takes 21 days to break a habit.

The benefits of being free from the sugar addiction:

*Less Brain Fog *Less High's and Low's with Energy

*Stronger Immune System (to fight disease) *Weight Loss

*Healthier Blood Sugar Levels *Better Sleep

*Less Demonic Influence *Less Anger

*Healthier Teeth, Skin, and Nails *Less Yeast

*Less Bladder Infections, *A "Sweeter" Spirit

My Prayer: *"Dearest Lord and Savior, as you know, this sugar thing has been one of my hardest struggles. Please help me. Forgive me for my sneakiness and binging with sugar. Help me to make a good plan and stick to it. Please bind up any sugar demons that influence me and loose Your ministering helping angels. I need You!"*
Love Your Daughter, Liz

Your Prayer and Reflection: How can you be proactive in reducing or monitoring your sugar and carb consumption? What specific things can you do to help your family as well?

_____

_____

_____

Health and Choices

"You say, 'I am allowed to do anything'- but not everything is good for you. And even though 'I am allowed to do anything,' I must not become a slave to anything." — 1 Corinthians 6:12

*M*y natural path doctor stared at me from across his desk: "Elizabeth, I need to tell you that your blood work and lab results are **very** serious. You are severely anemic, and that's the tip of the iceberg."

He took a deep breath and continued with a steady voice, "There are some things we can do; however, you need to know that right now you are *'staring at a lion right between the eyes.'"* A lion? I thought. It took me aback.

"You need to dig within yourself and instinctually find what you can do to survive this. Your bleeding fibroids are draining you of all your life blood. You are going to have to make some choices here Elizabeth."

"What do you mean?" Eric and I asked in unison.

My naturopath doctor continued, "Well, after reviewing your health questionnaire, it reveals you're a real perfectionist. You will need to change the way you think. You will also need to re-evaluate everything you put into your body and everything you surround your body with. **Your choices impact your health.**"

Menopause - Estrogen - Fibroids

For months I had been suffering with bleeding fibroids connected to my pre-menopausal state at age forty-nine. One dramatic night in fact, I ended up in the hospital on the white tiled floor in the bathroom. I was in a pool of fibroid menstrual blood.

As I lay on the floor, I heard Eric yell, "She needs a transfusion!"

Suddenly, there was a group of doctors and nurses crowding around me, scooping me off the white and now red tile, carrying me to the gurney. In a matter of minutes, I was hooked up to an IV, oxygen, and an "O positive" blood drip.

This season of my life was very challenging. Eric and I were trying to raise four teenagers at once, I was bleeding like crazy, and we were trying to do remodels and pay the bills. I was haunted by what the doctor had told me about my choices impacting my health. That's when I decided to start looking even more closely at what we buy and eat, the products that we use in our home and on our bodies.

After much research I realized that I had a very heavy load of estrogen in my body. The estrogen culprits became clear. I had been on birth control pills (estrogen build-up) previously for ten years, drank alcohol steadily for many, many years before we quit, and was somewhat cavalier about food, cleaning products, body products, and managing stress. After the bleeding fibroid season of my life I have been able to reflect back and make positive changes.

A new body of research, called epigenetics, confirms what my natural path doctor told me about our decisions and choices directly impacting our health and well-being.

Epigenetics

We hear a lot about genetics and DNA and how we are born with certain "bad" genes. However, there is a new body of research, called Epigenetics that indicates that we are born

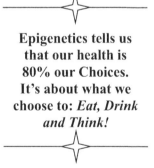

Epigenetics tells us that our health is 80% our Choices. It's about what we choose to: *Eat, Drink and Think!*

with a certain set of DNA and genes, however, our lifestyle choices can turn the genes "on" or "off". It is like a light switch. What we eat, drink, smoke, or even think can activate specific genes and conversely shut them off. It is 80% lifestyle, and 20% the genes. Duke University and Cleveland Clinic have done extensive studies on Epigenetics.

There are many YouTube videos to watch on the subject. Research Lorie Johnston, Epigenetics, CBN News for some excellent YouTube videos that explain *that our DNA is not our destiny.*

A powerful affirmation to recite:

"I am not my mother's disease; I am not my father's disease. I am Jesus' healed child; A child of God. I make good choices. I go forth in great health and wholeness by the grace of God and Jesus' act on the cross. By His Stripes I am healed."

A Choice for Spiritual Deliverance

Several years ago I decided to address some spiritual issues that were affecting my health and my marriage. I struggled for years with fear that I would get cancer again. I also struggled with issues of unforgiveness, binge eating, irritability, mistrust, snap-anger, annoyance, sloth, and judgementalism. These demons still rear their heads once in a while; however, after going through several deliverance healing sessions on the phone with Mr. Marion Knox I have had much greater peace.

Recently Eric and I were introduced to the concept of "Binding and Loosing." The Bible talks about this concept in Matthew 16 and 18. The idea is that we can pray in Jesus' name and authority asking God to "bind" up any specific demonic spirits in our own lives or in the lives of our loved ones. And in the name of Jesus Christ we can ask God to "loose" His ministering, helping angels. It helps to have two or three people in agreement doing the binding and loosing prayers, and it is most important to be persistent and long – term with these prayers. And, don't forget about fasting!

The friends that told us about binding and loosing just sent us a book called, *The Deliverance Manual.*

After opening the package, I split the book open and landed on page 218 where testimonies about deliverance were shared. Did you know that Jesus spent 1/3 of His ministry casting out demons and healing the afflicted? Why do we not hear about this today? We can just look around and see that demons and the devil are very busy at work.

One testimony in the red Deliverance manual revealed a woman struggling with food. She asked Jesus to cast out the demon called, "I Like to Eat." She knew obedience was better than sacrifice. She knew how to eat but was not doing it. God revealed to her that food can be divided into two groups: God's and devil's. Devil's food includes: sweets to excess, junk food, and liquids which are mostly empty calories.

Here is her summary of God's wisdom on food:

1. Eat fruits and vegetables, including leafy greens.
2. Do not eat much meat – three or four servings weekly.
3. Don't eat unless you truly need to.
4. Don't let others stuff you.
5. Seldom eat sweets.
6. Almost never eat junk food.
7. Remember those whose God is their belly.
8. Cook all foods simply.
9. Only use healthy fat and cut fat from meats.

I recommend the short, practical book, *The Secrets to Deliverance* by Alexander Pagani. Demonic influences and strongholds can be broken!

Good Choices vs. Bad Choices

Super model Kathy Ireland was a classmate of mine while growing up in Santa Barbara, California.

In her book, *Powerful Inspirations* she says, "We insist on a safe, healthy, loving atmosphere for our kids. One choice we made was that for family events and large parties at our home, we don't serve alcohol...our parties seem to end a lot earlier than they used to, we have much more fun..."

Not only that but Kathy resigned from her job promoting Anheuser Busch Beer Company, because as she states, "as I thought about it, I started to recognize that alcohol has had a negative impact on people I love over the years. I no longer felt comfortable promoting a product that has caused so much pain for so many families either by alcohol abuse, drunk driving, or other drinking/health-related issues."

Jesus First Strategy:

"Good Choices have Good Results-

Bad Choices have Bad Results."

We have choices about what we eat and drink and we also have choices about our attitude. Kathy says, "My Mom is the most positive person I know." When I was younger, she used to say that, "an optimist is someone who wakes up and says, 'Good morning, Lord' and a pessimist is someone who wakes up and says, 'Good Lord, it's morning.'"

Some decisions we make in life seem so innocent at the time. When we hear that tanning beds can cause skin cancer, we might brush it off and say it is pretty small odds, however...

Kelly, a beloved school teacher had gone to a tanning booth for many years. She had lovely tanned skin, beautiful fingernails, and was always well put together. She taught 6th grade English and the kids loved her. Some even had a *crush* on her because she was such a pretty teacher. At the age of 50 she reported to school one day with dire news. Kelly had melanoma. It had started in her scalp. She had surgery and chemotherapy, but she died within 6 months of the diagnosis.

The last email she sent out to friends and family Kelly said, "I love you all, please do not lay in tanning beds. I believe they caused my cancer."

Sometimes we don't even realize we are making unwise choices. Thankfully we can learn from other people's experiences.

Several years ago right after receiving my breast cancer diagnosis, I was struggling with the medical treatment options. After praying, God brought a wise friend's advice to my mind, "when in doubt, don't." Since I was having doubts about chemo, radiation, and surgery, I put the doctors off and turned to God in prayer and doing my own research. This landed me in the vitamin store where I began talking with the sales clerk. As I shared my diagnosis, I asked the clerk what supplements and dietary changes she suggested. As we chatted a woman came to the checkout counter with three bottles of Dr. Rath Healthy Cell Growth. And this is the story she told us:

"I overheard you talking about cancer. I am here today to tell you that several months ago my husband was diagnosed with stage 4 lung cancer. We 'bought time' with the doctors, and decided he would take a double dose of these Healthy Cell Growth Capsules before doing any medical treatments. After two months my husband went back in and they took an x-ray of his lungs and his lungs were perfectly clear! All cancer and tumors were gone. We also made some dietary changes, cutting way back on sugar and carbs."

That day at the health food store I purchased some of the Healthy Cell Growth Capsules as well as concentrated mushroom drops, vitamin E with Selenium, vitamin D, probiotics, green tea and fish oil with high EPA. I left the store with new hope, clarity, peace, and confirmation. I decided to put off surgery and treatment until I heard a clear word from God. In the meantime I took the natural supplements and started making some dietary and attitude changes. As mentioned earlier in this book, I was healed by God from my cancer. My goal is to turn to Jesus and God's food and Promises in His Word.

"Those who take personal responsibility for maintaining and enriching their physical bodies will live safe and healthy lives." Author of *Dead Doctors Don't Lie*—Dr. Joel Wallach

One Sunday, Eric and I found even more great wisdom, after singing at an Historic Carolina Church. After the service, I spoke with another Christian author, Sarah Tinsley. Sarah gave me a copy of her amazing book called, *Crying Angels* and one of her business cards. She mentioned her Dad always gave the best advice. They were listed on her card as follows:

Daddy's Top 10 Bits of Advice:

1. TRUST GOD
2. BE KIND
3. LIVE EACH MOMENT
4. DON'T WORRY
5. FOLLOW YOUR
   INSTINCTS
6. BE ADAPTABLE
7. VACATION OFTEN
8. APPRECIATE BEAUTY
9. LAUGH A LOT
10. TAKE A NAP

My Prayer: *"Thank you God for giving us free will to make choices. Forgive me for so many bad choices in the past, especially with eating, thinking, and lack of faith. I commit to changing now! I will make positive, healthy choices going forward. Thank You for helping me. I love You so!"*
Love Your Daughter, Liz

Your Prayer and Reflection: What choices can you make to have a healthier mind, body, and soul?

_____

_____

_____

Living Data, "Do's"

Proverbs 31 admonishes women to:
"Provide food for her household."

*W*hoever does the grocery shopping for your family holds life and death in the power of their hands and their grocery cart. A century ago, only one in a hundred people got cancer. Research now reveals that, "One in two people will be diagnosed with cancer at some point in their lives."

I encourage you to incorporate healthy changes along your journey right away. Remember, making big changes have *big* results and small changes have *small* results. God designed our bodies to stay healthy and heal naturally, when we take care of them. In several parts of the world there are still people living to 120 years old!

List of "Do's"
Health Builders and Cancer Fighting Tips

The following is a list of items to research on health and healing:

- **Drink tons of *Green Tea***-organic mostly decaf. A BIG Cancer fighter. Capsules are effective too.

- **Juicing and blender drinks**- consider juicing or blending organic vegetables and berries. Juicing extracts all the good nutrients and is a powerful boost to the immune system.

- **Exercise and Stretching:** the oxygen that exercising stirs up in the blood kills cancer cells. It is pretty simple; ***sugar feeds cancer and oxygen kills cancer.*** *Research this...*

- **Eat:** A Raw, organic, plant-based diet combined with Keto. For a Low Carb Diet these are the recommended percentages: Healthy Fat: 40 – 70%, Protein: 15 – 30%, Carbs: 15 -30%.

- **Eat a *salad*** with every lunch and dinner.

- **Sweat** out toxins by exercise, dry saunas or hot tubs.

- **Cruciferous vegetables** are big antioxidants! Including: broccoli, cauliflower, cabbage, & brussel sprouts. Note: If you haven't been eating many fruits and vegetables work them slowly into your diet so you don't get stomach cramps and bloating. Probiotics and Beano help with these symptoms.

- **Avocados**-filled with good stuff, very alkaline!

- **Lemons** are thought to be: "**Natural Chemotherapy.**" Research "Lemons fight cancer".

- **Alkaline-forming Foods fight cancer**: watermelon, citrus, avocados, vegetables, fermented food, Bragg's Apple Cider Vinegar (1-2 teaspoons daily). Remember the body responds to "acidic foods" with alkalinity. Eat Plant-Based Keto and try a Candida Cleanse.

- **Baking Soda** One teaspoon of baking soda in a glass of water daily, alkalizes the body. It is known to fight cancer.

- **Eat organic & Non-GMO**- It is suggested to get 80% of our food organic. Please rework your budget to get organic foods. Spend the money now, not later in the Hospital. At the bare minimum, get Non-GMO.

- **Prayer, Meditation and Fasting** - A **3 day fast** may rejuvenate cells in the immune system, starving defective cells. Eat a *"Light breakfast"*, or skip it, and do Intermittent fasting. Read ***Bragg's Healthy Lifestyle*** book for information. Prayer and meditation has been shown to reduce stress and inflammation in the body.

- *SIMPLIFY* - Eliminate toxic jobs, relationships, activities.

- **Gratitude** – Studies show that a gratitude practice combats depression and boosts overall well-being.

- **Do what you are "Called to do in life".** This brings peace. Everyone has a purpose in the world. Make plans.

- **Give yourself a lymph node massage.** Look it up.

- **SING!** Singing praises to God makes the enemy flee!!!

- **Eat lots of *garlic*, onion, fresh cilantro and parsley.** Fresh herbs detoxify.

- **Frankincense Oil**--rub some on your body for healing. I rub it where my mastectomy and abdominal scars are.

- **Deep Breathing**--- Remember cancer hates oxygen.

- **Rest!** 8 – 10 hours per night and a 20-minute nap.

- **Water:** Drink Eight – 8 ounces of <u>distilled or filtered</u> water a day (take your weight, divide it in half, and that is the number of ounces of water to drink daily). 1 glass with baking soda.

- **Beauty and cleaning products without toxins.** Buy organic, or make your own. Skin absorbs toxins into bloodstream. Use natural detergents.

- **Get Natural Sunscreen** (with zinc oxide) or make your own. See recipe in chapter 13.

- **Use Stainless steel pans** because black, nonstick pans emit a *toxic* odor when heated; enough to kill a small bird.

- **Use:** grape seed, olive oil or coconut oil when cooking. Do NOT heat olive oil beyond the smoking point.

- **Get 20-30 minutes of sun** every day for vitamin D.

- **Reflexology** – Hand and foot massages – removes toxins.

- **Remember WAIT on the Lord for direction. You have time!** Do NOT make any decisions out of fear or pressure if you get a bad diagnosis from the doctors.

- **Other top cancer fighting foods to incorporate in your diet include:** Maitake mushrooms, green juices, beets, dandelion root, leafy greens, coconuts, apples, carrots, beans, berries, salsa, hummus, cucumbers, nuts, seeds, turmeric and ginger root, dark chocolate, black tea, tomatoes, & fatty fish (wild caught).

Five Other Important Health Builders:
<u>CLEAN</u>: AIR—WATER—SUNSHINE—FOOD—EXERCISE

Natural Remedy Concepts:

Listed below are some natural remedy ideas that have been helpful to me and my family. If you have any of the below conditions please pray first for God's guidance. It is important that we not make natural supplements, our "god," any more than we make pharmaceuticals or doctors our "god." *Be aware that Pharma Drugs, like blood thinners, may not work well with some natural remedies.* I encourage you to research and consider the following:

- **Anxiety and Depression** – Vitamin D, Fish Oil with high EPA, St. John's Wort, Exercise, Proper Sleep, Keep Hydrated, Read the Psalms, Less: sugar, alcohol and processed foods. Repent of unforgiveness or sin. Seek deliverance. 30 minutes of sunshine daily lifts the mood!

- **Acid Reflux and Heart Burn** – Braggs Apple Cider Vinegar, Use a Wedge Pillow, No food or drink 3 hours before bed. Ginger, Loose clothing on the waist, Small meals, Bananas, Calcium. Reduce or avoid: caffeine, citrus, fried foods.

- **Autism** - Avoid or carefully space out vaccines as there are links to the MMR shot and autism. See the Documentary *Vaxxed* and research the "*Vaccine Friendly Plan*" by Dr. Paul Thomas. Avoid processed foods and sugar. Consider: Fish Oil, Magnesium, Probiotics, Turmeric.

- **Addiction** – Pray for Deliverance asking God to "bind up the *specific* addictive spirit and loose the healing helping angels." Consider the program 'Celebrate Recovery' through local churches. It takes 21 days to break a habit.

- **Back Pain** – Walk, swim, strengthen your core, hot compress. Good posture. Take Curcumin and use Uncle Bud's Ointment for Pain. Look up *Founder's Stretch* to avoid back surgery and try Pilates. Lose weight if needed.

- **Bladder and Kidney Infection** – 100% Cranberry Juice. D-Mannose. Hydrate. Kegel exercises. Avoid constipation. Reduce coffee, spicy foods, and alcohol. Cleanse area.
- **Basal Cell Carcinoma** – Eric cured area by applying 2 days of Frankincense Oil, then 4 days of Apple Cider Vinegar.
- **Breast Health, Menstrual Cramps, Fibroids, and Menopause** – Cut back on coffee, caffeine, bad fats, sugar, alcohol, dairy, red meat. Research: cruciferous vegetables, nuts, calcium, zinc, magnesium, selenium, vitamins B, C, and D, CoQ-10, Primrose, Candida Cleanse with *BAKING SODA* in a glass of water daily. Use natural deodorants and ultrasound or thermography rather than mammograms.
- **Constipation** – Try 100% aloe vera juice, ground flax seed, magnesium capsules, and probiotics. Drink lots of distilled water and eat lots of fruits and vegetables. Exercise and get things moving (jog). Smooth Move Tea. Avoid cheese.
- **COVID-19 (Virus), Common Cold & Immunity** – Sunshine, Vitamins D & C, Elderberry juice, zinc, garlic, oregano oil (natural antibiotic), sleep, moderate exercise, and green tea are helpful for any virus. "Vaccines are not very effective against viruses, as viruses *mutate quickly*" according to my Father, who is an Endocrinologist, M.D. Pray that the spirit of infirmity be cast out and that the healing, ministering angels be loosed! Pray for protection!
- **Diabetes** – Avoid sugars and starches. Read Dr. Gundry's books. Eat good fats, garlic, onions, *cinnamon,* cloves, turmeric, and ginger tea. Keep a healthy weight. Exercise.
- **Digestive Issues, IBS, and Leaky Gut** – Probiotics, Keto-Plant based diet. Avoid dairy/lactose. Reduce gluten. Eat a high fiber diet and eat apples and ground flax seed. Drink lots of water and reduce stress. Research Aloe Vera juice. *Remember, 80% of our health is in our gut!*

- **Ear Issues** – Research olive oil, mullein oil, garlic, silver gel by Silverbiotics. Use warm compress. Avoid Q-tips.
- **Eye Floaters** –Bilberry, L-Glutathione and Taurine, Olive Oil extract. Eric's disappeared with these!
- **Fibromyalgia** – Restorative sleep, reduce stress, work on posture, aerobic exercise, ice trigger points. Deliverance.
- **Gallbladder** – We have "passed" many stones with gallbladder flush: olive oil and lemon juice. Try "Stone Free Capsules" and apply a combination of Frankincense and almond oil on skin at sore gut area. Manually massage gut area. Reduce the following: fried, processed, fast foods.
- **Gout** – Reduce alcohol and rich foods like red meat. Try 100% cherry juice, apple cider vinegar. Baking Soda- Water.
- **Headaches**: peppermint oil rubbed on temples. Hydrate!
- **High Blood Pressure and High Cholesterol** – Magnesium/Calcium in a 2:1 ratio. Exercise and maintain healthy weight. Take Curcumin/Turmeric and Co Q-10. Eat almonds and research Braggs apple cider vinegar. Drink ginger, green and black tea and eat raw garlic. Omega 3 fish oils. Avoid saturated fats.
- **Memory** – Research Turmeric/Curcumin and Gingko Biloba, and high EPA fish oil supplement.
- **Osteoporosis** –Weight bearing exercises & healthy diet. Calcium, Magnesium, and Garlic. Avoid: caffeine, tobacco, pharmaceuticals & alcohol (they leach calcium from bones). Lose weight if needed.
- **Sciatic Nerve Pain** – Curcumin capsules and try Pilates.
- **Sexual Libido and Dryness** – Keep the bedroom for loving and sleeping only. Avoid discussing kids, in-laws, and money in the bedroom. Use coconut oil or Aloe Vera organic lubricant. Consider the exotic Ylang Ylang oil.
- **Skin/Hair Problems** – Vitamin D, and E. Keep hydrated

with 8 glasses of distilled water a day. Use organic, natural sunscreens only. Try almond, or coconut oil on skin and hair. Try a Hair, skin, nails capsule or gummy, or Biotin. Avoid or reduce alcohol; it dries skin and hair.

- **Sleep Issues** - Research the following: Magnesium - Calcium supplement, melatonin, and lavender oil. Read your Bible before bed and pray with your spouse. Keep a healthy sleep schedule and a cool, quiet, dark room. Avoid/reduce R rated movies, news and computers.
- **Sore Muscles** – Rub muscles with lavender, frankincense, and almond oils, or "Uncle Bud's Oil." Warm Epsom Salt Bath, Hot tub or sauna. Rest, ice, and heat.
- **Sore Throat**- Hot water with honey and lemon. Throat coat tea, gargle with warm salt water. Oregano oil. Organic *Elderberry* Zinc lozenges.
- **Thyroid Issues** – Curcumin supplement, Thyroid Care Capsule. Coconut, lavender, and frankincense oils. Ginger, green tea, apple cider vinegar, flax seed, walnuts, vitamin B, a healthy diet, and a multi-mineral capsule. Research lymph node massage. Avoid pharmaceuticals.
- **Tooth Pain and Canker sores** – Clove oil applied directly to the tooth and gum for pain. Rinse your mouth with hydrogen peroxide. Research "Coconut oil pulling". Myrrh.
- **Ulcers** – Studies shows that drinking lots of water often gets rid of stomach ulcers. Reduce stress along with spicy, tomato, citrus, alcohol and dairy foods. Consume cabbage and chamomile tea (natural antibiotic).
- **Yeast Infections** – Avoid sugar, carbs, dairy, beer, wine, cheese, birth control pills, antibiotics, tampons, tight clothing and douching. Keep the area dry; use blow dryer briefly. Wear cotton panties, and apply coconut oil.

Goodies from God's Garden

- **Elderberries** – for colds, flu, strong antiviral properties.
- **Cilantro, Dandelion Tea, and Parsley** – big detoxifiers.
- **Oregano Oil** – to fight off colds (a natural antibiotic).
- **Myrrh Oil** – mouth sores and inhibits cancer cell growth.
- **Clove Oil** – tooth Aches.
- **Tea Tree Oil** – skin infections.
- **Lavender Oil**– rest and sore muscles.
- **Extra Virgin Olive Oil** – cancer fighter and good for the heart *(do not heat past smoking point because it generates toxic fumes and free radicals which are harmful)*.
- **Cayenne Peppers** – for the heart.
- **Frankincense oil**- cancer fighter- see Chapter 13.
- **Epsom Salts** – taking a bath with Epsom salts pulls toxins out of your body.
- **CBD Oil** – It has been shown to stop cancer cell growth according to Penn State researchers (it's the extracted oil that does not make you "high"). Also research Black Salve.
- **Turmeric Oil**: May help fight breast cancer, colon cancer and leukemia. **Curcumin** is concentrated Turmeric.
- **Vitamin D3** – cancer fighter and mood elevator.
- **Fish oil, with high EPA** – for depression and heart issues.
- **St John's Wort** – for depression, anxiety, and nerves.
- **Magnesium** – to help relax the nervous system, reduce anxiety, and lowers blood pressure (taken daily it has lowered mine 20 points).
- **Ginger and Garlic** – two super foods!
- **Aloe Vera** – drink several ounces a day as a natural antibiotic, anti-inflammatory, and a relaxant of the digestive tract or topical for burns.

- **Castor Oil Compresses** – use on your body nearest to the location of disease to suck out toxins.
- **Broccoli sprouts and Watercress** – combats cancer.

Top 12 Tips to give a Friend Diagnosed with Cancer:

1. **Buy yourself some time** – Let the doctors or naturopath (natural Doctor) know you need time to prayerfully consider all of your options (Trust God not man). Give the doctors a "hold-harmless" letter – See Chapter 6.
2. **Pray to God for wisdom.** God says He gives wisdom to those who ask. LISTEN to His promptings. Meditate.
3. **Repent of Sins and Forgive Others...** it's Biblical for healing. Remove stumbling blocks. Ask a church elder for prayer anointing with **healing oil.** *When Ye Pray, Believe!*
4. **Friends and Family** – tell them what you need. For example: prayers, food, research, errands, encouragement, extra space, no guilt or pressure.
5. **Music and Bible Verses** – surround yourself with His healing promises. Meditate on His Word. Believe it!
6. **Research**- your options. Consider consulting with Naturopath or Holistic doctors. Get Second Opinion.
7. **Rest, Sunshine & Exercise.** Claim time alone with God.
8. **Food** – change the terrain of the inside of your body. Slowly transition to an organic plant-based Keto lifestyle creating an alkaline environment that is hostile to Candida and fast-growing defective cells (cancer). **Consider Fasting.**
9. **Cleanse Environment**: use only natural products on your body, home and car. Avoid 5G, chemtrails, toxic food and water. Eat and drink clean.
10. **Supplements**: a good multi-vitamin with minerals, Boswellia (frankincense), Dr. Rath Healthy Cell Growth

Capsules, Vitamin E and Selenium, Vitamin B, D, High doses of Vitamin C, Magnesium, CO-Q10, fish oil (high EPA) Probiotics, Green Tea, Melatonin, and Curcumin. **IMPORTANT:** *Rub **Frankincense Oil*** directly on the skin near the site of disease four times daily and on navel.

11. **Avoid Sugar, Carbs, and Alcohol & drink Alkaline or Distilled Water** (with lemon or 1 tsp of baking soda).

12. **Most Importantly**: Believe that God Can Heal You! Remember Jesus Never turned Anyone away who came to Him for Healing. Come Boldly before God with Great Expectation. Recite: *"I will not die but live so I can proclaim the good works of the Lord!"*

One More Big Tip: Consider changing your Health Insurance to a *Faith-Based Health Care Provider*; such as Christian Health Care Ministry, Liberty Health Share, Medi-Share, or Samaritan Ministries. We save big money!

My Prayer: *"Dear God, thank You for providing us with so many healing remedies and foods. YOUR CREATION IS AMAZING!"*
            Love Your Daughter Forever, Liz

Your Prayer and Reflection: What can you incorporate into your life for better health?

_____

_____

_____

Living Data "Don'ts"

List of "Don'ts" – Avoid or Reduce

*W*e have the opportunity to make healthy choices for ourselves and steer away from choices that may be destructive. In the Western Countries especially we need our radar up! The following is a list for you to consider and research:

- **White Foods** - Most white food is not healthy. I did a kitchen cleansing and tossed: white rice, white pasta, white sugar, white flour, most white dairy, white tortillas, white bread and white artificial sweeteners.
- **Sugar** - Refined sugar, sugar substitutes, corn syrup and its sisters are listed in Chapter 15: Sugar Feeds Cancer.
- **Regular soda**- Linked to cancer; All sodas are addictive.

- **All Pharmaceutical Drugs have negative side effects** - Please research and pray for direction before taking drugs. You have time. Most have *aluminum* which causes delirium or *Alzheimer's disease*. Check out God's natural remedies.
- **Illegal Drugs** – Avoid.
- **Chemotherapy** – A landmark study shows that half of cancer patients are killed by chemo – not the cancer. Pharmacists who deal with chemotherapy pills have a higher rate of cancer.
- **Flu shot** – it contains 25mg of mercury, formaldehyde, and can cause blood and lymphatic disorders. Flu shots only work on 1 in 100 strains of the flu due to mutations.
- **Vaccines** –The *"Vaccine Compensation Program"* has paid out over 4.5 Billion Dollars to injured parties. Many studies show they cause autism, or even death. I have one dear friend Dawn, whose baby died right after vaccinations. We have friends and relatives whose infants have suffered from seizures, autism, violent food allergies and even polio after vaccines were given.
- **Smoking Cigarettes, Marijuana, Juuling/Vaping, E-cigarettes** – The AMA called for an immediate ban on all electronic cigarettes and vaping due to lung illnesses. Marijuana is linked to Psychosis, strokes, de-motivation, and lung cancer (according to Web MD). *Lung cancer is the #1 cancer killer in America*.
- **Alcohol/Wine** – is linked to several cancers including liver, breast, and colon. The more you drink the higher your risk. The chemical your body produces when it metabolizes alcohol damages DNA. Studies show most California wineries use *toxic arsenic* for flavor and cancer-causing *sulfites* for preservatives.

- **Obesity** – and a **Sedentary Lifestyle** have connections to cancer and many other diseases.
- **Donuts & Pastries** – watch for carbs, toxins and sugars.
- **Coffee-Mate** or creamers- read toxic ingredient list.
- **Diet soda** – Aspartame in diet soda is linked to Leukemia and Lymphoma in a Landmark Study on humans.
- **Artificial Sweeteners** – may lead to headaches, dizziness, rashes, digestive problems, and long-term diseases.
- **Canned food** – look for BPA free liners. Nearly 40% contain BPA, a chemical linked to birth defects and cancer.
- **Aluminum Foil** – **can** leach into food and become toxic.
- **Ensure Nutrition Drinks and Energy Drinks**– they are full of chemicals, read ingredient list.
- **GMO's and Non-Organic Foods** – Genetically Modified Organisms are natural foods that have been tampered with. Buy Non-GMO, organic whenever possible! If something is listed as organic, it is automatically Non-GMO. However, *Non-GMO* does not necessarily mean it is organic. Most produce is heavily sprayed with chemicals, and may cause disease.
- **Canola Oil, Corn Oil and Cotton Oil** – made from GMO crops and are linked to inflammation, heart disease, and stroke. Use Olive oil, Coconut oil and Avocado oil
- **Processed Foods** – have been linked to many cancers. Try to eat and prepare foods in their most natural state.
- **Fast Food** – toxic, addictive ingredients are added to many fast foods. See the Documentary, *"Super Size Me."* Also, beware of carcinogenic fats, sugars, carbs, and corn syrup.
- **Acid-forming Foods to Avoid or Reduce**: sugar, alcohol, meat, coffee, soft drinks, potato chips, processed food, ice-cream, white pasta, white rice, white bread.

- **Pork and BBQ Ribs** – World Health Organization reports that BBQ ribs, bacon, and hotdogs are just as cancer causing as smoking cigarettes.
- **'Blackened' foods** - trim off the black carcinogenic BBQ charred parts. Applies to meat, poultry, and vegetables.
- **Processed Lunch Meats** - including salami, pepperoni, and hotdogs, smoked and preserved foods. Most have Nitrates that may cause cancer. Try tuna or egg sandwiches.
- **Red meats** may also be harmful due to hormones. Try *Grass-fed* instead.
- **Shellfish** – is commonly dipped in Bisodium Sulfite, a toxic chemical. Eating crab landed me in the hospital twice from a reaction to the toxins. Reduce or avoid shellfish.
- **Limit Dairy and Soy** – both have links to hormonal cancers (at the very least make sure dairy is rBST free). Goat or Almond milk and goat cheese are better options. In moderation, non-GMO Soy is o.k. - *Read food labels!*
- **Super-hot Coffee or Tea**- has ties to esophageal cancer.
- **Excessive Sun/Lack of Sun** – 20-30 minutes a day is good for you to get Vitamin D, but more than that is not.
- **Sunscreen**- is toxic unless it is organic and natural. Refer to chapter 13 for a DIY healthy sunscreen.
- **Tanning Beds** – Remember the story about Kelly in Chapter 16. They can cause cancer...
- **Dust** – vacuum floors regularly, clean with white vinegar. Check into getting an air purifier.
- **Permanent Hair Dye** - and chemical straighteners may increase breast cancer risk a new study reveals.
- **Hand Sanitizers** – typically have chemical toxins. The toxins enter the bloodstream and can cause disease. Please make your own, or use organic hand sanitizers.
- **Chlorine in Pools and Hot Tubs** – Make sure to rinse off.

An effective hot tub treatment is 1 cap of "Thieves Cleaner" by Young Living and 10 drops of lavender or geranium essential oil twice a week. Consider installing a chlorine filter on your shower head or faucets.

- **Makeup and Lotions with Parabens** (toxic chemicals) – Research Beautycounter, Lemongrass Spa, or Young Living to find more natural options. Read your labels.
- **'Protective Face Masks'**- may cause carbon dioxide poisoning and bacterial pneumonia. CDC and WHO initially said that masks are *not* effective, and now they have changed their recommendations. Studies show that exposure to some germs is important to build immunity.
- **Deodorant/Anti-perspirant** – many contain aluminum which is linked to cancer. Do your best to use organic.
- **Underwire Bras** – buy without wires, or remove them.
- **Breast Implants**: may cause or hide cancer.
- **Laundry Detergents** – many have dyes and perfumes that can be carcinogenic. Try to use Free & Clear detergents or Castile Soap or Dr. Bronner's.
- **Household Cleaners** – often have toxins. Use 1 cup white vinegar, 2 to 3 cups of water and 1 teaspoon of liquid dish detergent instead. A few drops of essential oil optional.
- **Plug-ins, Febreze & Other Chemical Air Fresheners** – Avoid. Instead use Pure Citrus Orange Air Freshener (100% orange oil – this can also be used to clean leather).
- **New Furniture and Rugs** - many rugs and fabrics have been treated with toxic fire-retardant spray. New kitchen cabinets can emit poisonous Melamine and formaldehyde. Try to avoid and air out at the least.
- **Hot cars emit toxic fumes**- Air them out!
- **Gasoline Fumes**- are toxic. Keep your distance.
- **Avoid Estrogen**- in birth control pills and body fat.

Estrogenic foods to avoid are: conventional meat and dairy as they have strong links to hormonal cancers. Also, avoid or reduce soy, sugar, preservatives, processed food and beverages, grains, and beer. Toxic Environmental sources include: plastics, personal care products, pharmaceuticals, Styrofoam products, pesticides, typical detergents, cleaners, canned goods and air fresheners. My breast cancer was linked to estrogen as were my bleeding fibroids. Learn from my mistakes.

- **Microwave**- Avoid it! It deforms the molecular structure of food, and may create abnormal changes in the blood and immune systems. Plastic leaches toxins into your food when micro-waved. Glass is preferable. If you do need to use the microwave stand at least 5 feet away. Microwave popcorn is carcinogenic. Use your cook-top!
- **Root Canals**- research the connection between root canals, infections, migraines and cancer.
- **Talcum Powder** – there are many class action law suits because of the link to cancer. I just met a lady whose mother has ovarian cancer due to using talcum powder.
- **Bug Sprays** – often have toxic ingredients especially Deet. Get organic or make your own.
- **Fluoridated Toothpaste** - in 1997, the USDA stated that all fluoride toothpastes must carry a poison warning on the label. Look for natural toothpastes.
- **Avoid Fluoridated, Chlorinated Water** - Buy distilled water, a Countertop Distiller, Zero Water filter, or Berkey water filter. Also, make sure to use BPA free bottles. Studies show that Fluoride is linked to many diseases. Chlorine is linked to rectal and bladder cancers. In our home, we do a variety of distilled water, filtered Water; *Zero & Berkey*.
- **Chem Trail Air** – avoid "chem-cough" and toxic exposure.

Stay inside on heavy spray days when the sky is white. Research: Geoengineeringwatch.org. Fresh air and oxygen are critical to good health. Consider an air purifier.

- **Cell phones, 5G, Wi-Fi, Smart Meters** –Avoid getting a 5G cell phone or living near a 5G cell tower or receptor/receiver. Use speaker phone: Avoid cell phone against your ear, or in your pocket or bra, avoid Earbuds or ear Bluetooth. Studies have shown that cell phones by the ear or body may cause cancer. 5G is 100 times stronger than 4G. Buy a Wi-Fi router guard, and turn router off at night. Use an RFID phone case. Turn your phone off at night and consider getting an RF Meter. We have lost two friends to brain cancer as a result of cell-phone radiation (they were both 24/7 in sales on cell phones). Finally, "Smart Meters" may cause cancer; Request to "Opt Out." Use an Analog Electric Meter.

- **Unnecessary X-rays, Mammograms** - radiation can build up in the body. Look into Thermography or Ultrasounds instead. One doctor said that mammograms cause 10 cancers for every 1 it catches.

- **Ultrasounds during pregnancy**: may harm baby.

- **"Roundup"/Glyphosate - Gardening/Yard Spray** – Roundup weed killer causes cancer. Buy *organic foods* as almost all crops are sprayed with glyphosate/Roundup (or other pesticides), especially wheat and corn. A new study found that organic diets quickly reduce the amount of Glyphosate in people.

- **Avoid Plastic Containers** when re-heating food. Plastic is cancer-causing/carcinogenic. When heated, or scratched, it seeps into food or drink. Use BPA free bottles.

- **Stress, Unforgiveness, Dysfunctional Relationships, Dehydration, Lack of Rest, Lack of exercise,** are all Cancer Risk Factors according to Recent Studies.

- The *Dirty Dozen* is a list of fruits and vegetables with the most pesticides. Be sure to **BUY *the following fruits and vegetables Organic***: *strawberries, spinach, nectarines, apples, peaches, pears, cherries, grapes, celery, tomatoes, kale, potatoes.* Note: Look up this list yearly as it changes. Foods with thinner skins absorb the most pesticides.

Pharmaceutical Drugs and Their Detrimental Side Effects
Here are several that impacted me—my family or friends.
Please Research:

- **Anti-depressants** – Weight gain, lethargy, anxiety, suicidal thoughts and or suicide, lower sex drive, constipation, fatigue. I personally suffered with several of these side effects when on Paxil and later, Lexapro.

- **Cholesterol Drugs (statins)** – A study published in the *American Journal of Physiology*, states that statins advance the "process of aging", and increase the risk of diabetes and memory loss, which mimics Dementia and Alzheimer's.

- **Antibiotics** – Try Oregano Oil capsules or drops rather than antibiotics. Avoid Cipro at all costs. My friend took it for a bladder infection was paralyzed from the waist down. She still suffers with major nerve damage 10 years later. Doctors told her that nerve damage/paralysis one of the "listed" side effects. Other antibiotic side effects include: wipes out the good bacteria in your gut, yeast infections, skin rashes.

- **Diabetes Medications** – May cause weight gain, skin reactions, headaches, and possibly cancer.

- **Acid Reflux Medications such as Pepcid (Anti Acids)** - Confusion, hallucinations, agitation, and lack of energy.
- **Thyroid Medication** – Weight gain, tremors, hair loss, depression, irritability, low energy.
- **Blood Pressure Medications** – Nagging cough, confusion, low energy.
- **Chemotherapy** – Fatigue, hair loss, constipation, vomiting, dry mouth, numbness in hands and feet, hearing and balance loss, weakens your natural defenses, kills the good cells and the bad cells, depression, death.
  Dr. Harden B. Jones of UC Berkeley did a study on cancer and found:
  "People who refused Chemotherapy live over a dozen years longer than people taking chemotherapy. Patients with breast cancer rejecting conventional therapy live four times longer than those who follow the system."
- **Radiation** – Difficulty swallowing and breathing, breast or nipple soreness, fatigue, nausea, long term damage to your body, urinary and sexual problems, depression, disintegration of bones and organs. One friend had radiation on her pelvis and her bones started to crumble.
- **Birth Control Pills** – Adds a cumulative build-up of estrogen in the body. It contributed to my breast cancer and bleeding fibroids. Also: headaches, mood changes, decreased libido, breast tenderness. I was on them for 10 years and gained 10 pounds and when I went off, 10 pounds melted off. My friend's 24-year-old daughter suffered a stroke and the doctor sheepishly admitted that it was a side effect from the birth control pills.
- **Pain Killers and Opioids** – Addiction, constipation, nausea, clouded thinking, and slowed breathing. Divorce.

185

My Prayer: *"Dear God, thank You for providing us natural remedies and cures and for revealing to us things that are harmful. Give us wisdom and self-control to make wise choices."*

Love Your Daughter Forever, Liz

Your Prayer and Reflection: Based on the information in this chapter, what can you reduce or eliminate in your life for better health?

_____

_____

_____

What about Miracles?

"He performs wonders that cannot be fathomed,
Miracles that cannot be counted." — Job 5: 8-9

Parker suffered with deafness and a recent blindness in one eye. As an elementary school student, being deaf is difficult but losing eyesight is devastating. The following is an account of a miracle that God performed.

Parker's parents, Brad and Jessica, shared with their adult Sunday School small group their huge concerns for their energetic, adopted son Parker. My dear friend Laura, was at the Bible-study and chimed in:

"Let's remember that God is the Great Healer and can heal Parker, and I believe we should pray for his healing. We often forget: *God Still Heals!*"

Immediately, the group responded with faith for healing.

In expectation of a miracle, the prayers flowed fervently for the healing of Parker's nearly blind eye.

A few days later, Jessica posted this blog:

"We went to the eye exam and discussed the urgency we had been faced with. We reviewed the findings with the technician and she began the exam. She started with the good eye. Then she switched the patch. I think we all took a breath at the same time. Parker began to rattle the letters off. I was looking at the board and back at him...board, then him...board, then him.

Parker began to grin ear to ear. I knew instantly that he could see them. Brad and I knew we had just seen God heal him with this miracle.

Then Parker smiled saying, 'I can see them!'

I really couldn't get out of the office fast enough. We got in the car and headed to go purchase Parker's glasses. The quiet little boy that was there this morning was a character of the past. The Parker that is loud and loves life was back.

'**Parker?**' I gently said.

'**What?**' he replied.

'**Do you think that God healed you in there?**'

He looked over with his sunglasses behind his clear glasses and grinned big and said:

'**I KNOW HE DID.**'"

God still performs miracles! Only believe!

Often, when we take the focus off ourselves and pray for others with healing expectation, we will find God's miracles!

Faith and Miracles

I recently heard an analogy on T.V. regarding faith and miracles. The Evangelist said, "When we fill an ice cube tray with water and put it in the freezer, we expect that it will turn it into ice cubes. We don't stand at the refrigerator and pray and pray for it to freeze we just expect and believe it will. Likewise, when the conditions are right with our faith, and ask the Lord for healing—we can expect it."

God's healing doesn't always come the way we anticipate it; the conditions need to be right. For example, I may

Jesus First Strategy:

"The Biggest Miracle of All;
Jesus Died on the Cross for our Sins!"

fervently pray for a friend to get an "A" on a math test, but if my friend hasn't studied at all, she probably won't get that "A". Likewise, if the conditions for our healing aren't right with our heart, our mind or our body we will not be able to pray with Holy Spirit conviction in our heart for that healing and miracle.

However when the conditions are right, we will be able to pray with great conviction, great hope and faith, believing and receiving Gods healing promises. In fact we are called to live in relationship with God, and He wants to be our best friend and confidant. He wants us to work with Him, in partnership. *"Indeed our fellowship is with the Father and His son Jesus Christ"* (1 John 1:3).

God doesn't need our help, but He loves it when we do our best to please and obey Him. We can do this by cleansing our minds of negative thoughts and replacing them with Bible promises on healing. We can talk to God during the day and pray to Him. We can study His word in the Bible. We can sing praises, hymns and take good care of the temples He has given us.

Jesus says, He wants "none to perish" and in the Bible He says He wants us to have abundant and healthy lives. Remember, the biggest miracle of all was Jesus dying on the cross for our sins so that we might be forgiven and have eternal life!

When we step squarely on the promises of God and have faith and believe in those promises it casts away the doubt. Jesus said *"I came to give you life and life in abundance..."* and *"Take up your cross and follow me."* And *"I can do all things through Christ who strengthens me."* and His Word also says, *"I called upon the Lord and He healed me."* And in Mark 16 Jesus said, *"They will lay hands on the sick and they will recover."*

Greg Laurie, the famous evangelist, shared this story, "What about the man who comes to you and says, 'I believe in God but I don't believe in miracles?'" Greg Laurie's answer to that is "It's not a problem because sooner or later you're going to need one!" And that often is what will happen. On the other hand there are a lot of people who do believe in miracles and want miracles but don't want the trials that go with them. Often miracles and healings are done in God's Way and on His timeline, not ours.

A lot of people believe in the Bible. Many people believe in miracles that happen in the Bible, but they stop short in believing that God can do one for them.

How to prepare ones Heart for Miracles:

1. Confession of sin – Apologize to God for our short comings and ask for his forgiveness and commit to changing our heart and our ways.

2. Recognize God's healing power. **Study and memorize** His scriptures on healing.

3. Commit to doing our best to care for our bodies, hearts, and souls going forward.

4. Believe God's going to do it for you – know that healing power is activated by faith and fervent prayers of the righteous.

5. Remember, Jesus paid the price on the cross for us. The bread of communion represents healing of the body and the wine represents healing of the soul. "By His stripes we are healed."

6. Act on faith. Live as if we are healthy and healed.

7. Renounce the kingdom of darkness – Trust God, not man. Pray that the demons be 'bound' and the healing helping angels be 'loosed.' Speak directly to the sickness. Saying things like, "Spirit of cancer, fear and doubt I rebuke you! In the name of Jesus Christ, be gone!"

8. The Holy Spirit is crucial to the healing process. Singing praise songs, worship and fervent prayer are critical, as they stir the Holy Spirit within us.
   "If the Spirit of Him who raised Jesus from the dead dwells in you, He will also give life to your mortal bodies through His Spirit in you," (Romans 8:11).
   Remember, God's promises are "alive and active" now, and Jesus is *with us* until the end!

A Few Miracles in the Bible – Look Them Up!

Miracles of Jesus	Matt.	Mark	Luke	John
Jesus Healed a leper	8:1	1:40	5:12	
Healed Peter's mother-in-law	8:14	1:29	4:38	
Calmed a storm on the Sea of Galilee	8:23	4:35	8:22	
Delivered the demon possessed at Gadara	8:28	5:1	8:26	
Healed the lame man	9:1	2:1	5:18	
Healed a woman with an issue of blood	9:18	5:25	8:43	
Raised Jairus's daughter	9:23	5:22	8:41	
Fed 5000 people	14:15	6:35	9:12	6:1
Walked on the Sea of Galilee	14:22	6:47		6:16
Healed an epileptic boy	17:14	9:14	9:37	
A miraculous catch of fish			5:4	
Healed a stooped-over woman			13:11	
Healed ten lepers			17:11	
Healed a lame man at pool of Bethesda				5:1
Healed a blind man				9:1
Raised Lazarus				11:38
Jesus Raised from dead	28:6	16:6	24:6	20:5

A Fireworks Miracle

Eric and I decided to take a few hours break from our book writing and home remodeling. Eric had two older guitars he wanted to sell, so we headed downtown to a Christian music store. The woman behind the counter had an angelic quality to her. Her long blond hair and soft blue eyes made her very approachable. I asked her, "How has God been working in your life lately?" She shared this story:

"Several years ago I was diagnosed with stage four cancer. There were grape size tumors lining my throat and I could barely swallow."

I leaned in closer as she whispered, "One day after meeting with my doctor I came home and prayed. I pleaded, 'Lord if you want me to live please take this cancer away...'" She continued, "Later that week I was at a small church service where they were serving communion. As I swallowed the elements, I felt fireworks in my throat. It wasn't painful. It felt like bursting popping fireworks... that's the only way I can describe it." I felt a special kinship with this dear woman as I thought back to my cancer deliverances.

She went on, "Later that week I went back to my doctor preparing for surgery. The doctor looked down my throat and did some more x-rays and said 'what happened to you Laurel the tumors are gone!' Then I told him about the communion and fireworks in my throat, and we both agreed it was nothing short of a miracle." I touched Laurel's hand and thanked her for sharing her amazing testimony.

I told her about my three cancers and deliverance. As we were heading out Eric dashed to the car and grabbed a copy of my testimonial book, *Floored and Delivered* and gave it to her. I gave her a big hug as we left.

Jesus First Strategy

"The diagnosis from the Doctor is never final… We serve a powerful God that miraculously heals!"

We so often hear of miracles as we travel and share the Good News. It builds faith and reminds us that the diagnosis from the Doctor is never final. We serve a powerful God that miraculously heals!

God's Gift of a new Song

As I was wrapping up this book, I awoke one morning with a song on my heart. God gave me the words and wove scriptures into this Healing Song. I hopped out of bed, wrote down the words, then Eric put piano music to it. With love and gratitude in my heart, I now share this healing song with you, my precious readers. Visit *YouTube: Eric and Elizabeth Soldahl* for the song live.

The song is based on the following favorite Bible Story that is found in Matthew, Mark, and Luke:

A woman had a flow of blood for twelve years, and had suffered many things from many physicians. She spent all that she had and was no better, but rather grew worse. She said, "If only I may touch His robe, I shall be made well." Pressing through the crowd, she touched His robe and immediately her fountain of blood was dried up and she was healed. Then Jesus turned to her, saying "Daughter, your faith has made you well. Go in peace, and be healed of your disease".

The Healing Song ~ *'Keeper of my Soul'*

God the Healer Mighty Lord!
Washes with His Holy Word
Restore our health—Heal our wounds
Sent Your Son to save the world— Keeper of my soul

Touched His robe and she believed
Through the crowd to be made clean
He turned to her, as healing flowed,
"Take heart, my daughter; your faith has made you
Whole!"

You're the Keeper of my soul
The One who makes me whole again
Savior on my burdened way
So I cling to Your robe – yes, I cling to Your robe
Until You take me home…

I am healed and I am whole,
I am healed, mind, body, soul,
I am healed and adored, Christ in me forevermore!

He says, Ask and Believe, you shall Receive.
Repent then by Grace, Jesus will save!

I touched His robe and I believed,
And now I stand and clearly see Jesus.
He said to me, "I love you so."
Faithful tears began to flow…
Jesus whispered, "Daughter your faith has made you
(I am healed) whole!"
Spoken softly as the song ends: *"He bore our sickness at*
the whipping post—By His stripes we are healed."

My husband, Eric, and I singing for U.S. Veterans, as "Musical Missionaries"

My Final Prayer: *"Dear Miracle Worker God, thank You for Your amazing Word and Your food. I praise You for all of the healing Miracles in my life and the lives of those around me. I anticipate more miracles based on your promises. I love You and am forever indebted and devoted to You!"*

Love Your Daughter, Liz

Your Prayer and Reflection: What miracles has God worked in *your* life?

_____

_____

_____

Dearest Precious Reader Friends,

Thank you for joining me on this journey. I pray that you have been encouraged in your faith through the stories, verses and inspirations shared in this book. I truly hope that you have fresh ideas to implement in your life, with God's Word and food. I offer you this healing blessing with love:

"May God restore your health and heal your wounds. May you have a great hope and future, may you confess your faults to one another and pray for one another that you may be healed. May you have an abundant life and excellent health until the day the Lord takes you home. And may Jesus whisper to you, 'Your faith has made you whole, Go in Peace and be healed of your affliction.'" 🩶

With Jesus' love, healing and faith, *Liz*

P.S. *"If you haven't already committed your life to God and would like to accept Jesus into your heart as your Lord and Savior please follow the A,B,C's explained at the end of Chapter 8."*

Delicious Recipes for Life!

*I*t's best to use **ORGANIC** ingredients whenever possible, for health and tastiest flavors in all recipes. Also use **Non-GMO** whenever possible. If a label says Organic it is automatically Non-GMO. If the label says Non-GMO, it *may or may not* be Organic.

Appetizers, Salads & Main Courses

1. Italian Cabbage Soup:
Ingredients:
- ½ head of cabbage chopped (or one bag shredded)
- 1 yellow onion chopped
- 4-5 cloves garlic minced
- 1 red, yellow or green bell pepper chopped (or ½ each)
- ½ bunch of celery chopped
- 2-3 cups of spinach chopped
- 1 large carton Cream of Tomato soup

- 1 large carton of organic vegetable or chicken broth
- Salt and pepper to taste
- Italian Herbs (1-2 T crushed between your fingers)
- ¼ cup olive oil
  Optional Ingredients:
- 2 Cups: organic, sautéed chicken- chopped into pieces, or rotisserie chicken chunks.
- ½ cup wild rice, or cauli-flowered rice, white beans, lentils, Italian parsley, any other veggies, 4 Bay leaves, hot sauce. Additional water if needed.

Instructions:
1. Sauté garlic and onion (optional). Put all ingredients into a large pot. Bring to a boil. Simmer for 40-60 minutes.
2. Dish up and top each bowl with a bit of grated cheese or a dollop of plain greek yogurt or avocado.

Tips:

-Freeze extra in glass containers, or share with a neighbor.

-Feel free to use whatever veggies you have. Cozy dinner in the fall or winter.

2. Krista's Best Turkey Chili
Ingredients:
- 1 pound ground turkey
- 1 carton organic chicken broth
- 1 Large can of chopped organic tomatoes
- 1 Large or medium can kidney beans, drained
- 1 small organic onion- chopped
- ½ yellow bell-pepper -chopped
- 2 cloves minced garlic
- 1tsp Tabasco or other hot sauce
- 1 Tablespoon Italian herbs

Instructions:
1. Cook meat in fry pan with olive oil and butter till brown (medium/low heat), breaking into chunks.
2. Add veggies and seasonings and cook a few minutes.
3. Put all ingredients into large pot and cook for about one hour.

Tips:

-I sometimes have little bowls of toppings, including: chopped avocado, plain greek yogurt, grated cheese, chopped green onion, black olives, or crushed tortilla chips.
-Freeze extra for a rainy day. This is a delicious, complete meal.

3. Keto Chicken Salad
Ingredients:
- ½ Organic Rotisserie chicken boned and chopped up
- ¼ purple onion finely minced (2 green onions works too)
- 2-3 stalks of celery finely minced
- 2 heaping tablespoons of organic mayonnaise
- 2 heaping tablespoons of plain greek yogurt. (or you may use all 4 T mayo if you prefer.)
- 1 teaspoon of mustard (I prefer Dijon)
- Black Pepper (to taste)

Instructions:
1. Mix all ingredients together in a bowl and serve along with a tossed salad or place a large scoop on one piece of Dave's Killer Bread, or Ezekiel Bread, toasted.

Tips:
-Sometimes I add in chopped artichokes, sweet pickles, dill weed, apples, grape halves, chopped pineapple or walnuts. A little tomato or berries on the side make for a colorful appetizing plate.
-You can add in 2 teaspoons curry powder to make "curry chicken salad".

4. <u>Keto Tuna Salad</u>
-Follow the Keto Chicken Salad recipe above, only replace Rotisserie chicken with 2 small or 1 large can of drained tuna.
Tips:
- Serve with a green salad, sauerkraut, pickles, kimchi. Or scoop tuna mixture on healthy bread and serve "Open Faced," or top with a couple slices of cheese and broil top in oven for a tuna melt.

5. <u>Keto Guacamole Dip:</u>
Ingredients:
- 3 large ripe avocados peeled & pitted (avocados should be somewhat soft, color dark, &stem should pop off easily)
- 5 cloves of garlic peeled and chopped fine or pressed
- 3 Tablespoons finely chopped Green onion (optional)
- 1/3 bunch cilantro chopped fine(optional)
- 1 medium tomato seeded chopped medium (optional)
- ½ lemon or lime squeezed
- Salt, pepper, and a dash of hot sauce to taste

Instructions:
1. Mash avocados in bowl.
2. Add all other ingredients and mix.
3. Served with veggie sticks (cucumber, celery, carrot) and or Organic Late July Chips.

Tips:
-Double or triple recipe for parties.
-May add one finely chopped jalapeno pepper (seeds removed).
-If there is any guacamole left over store it in a glass bowl with plastic wrap pressed tightly against the guacamole (no air to keep from going brown).
-Easy FAST Option: 1/3 jar of organic salsa, and 3 mashed avocados!

6. Keto Aioli Sauce:

Ingredients:
- ¾ cup organic mayonnaise
- 5 cloves garlic crushed through a garlic press or minced fine
- 2 ½ tablespoons lemon juice
- Salt and pepper to taste (1/2 teaspoon each)

Instructions:
1. Wisk all ingredients together.

Tips:
-Refrigerate at least ½ hour before serving.
-Sauce is delicious drizzled on cooked veggies, fish, chicken, hamburgers, or tossed on a green salad.
-May substitute ½ of mayonnaise with full fat Greek yogurt.

7. Cobb Salad:

Salad Ingredients:
- 4 cups organic mixed spring lettuce
- 2 tomatoes, quartered
- 2 avocados, pitted and sliced or cubed
- 2 cups cooked chicken, shredded (organic)
- 5 strips turkey bacon, cooked and cut small
- 2 hard-boiled eggs, quartered
- ½ cup goat cheese or blue cheese, crumbled

Instructions:
1. Cover the bottom of a large bowl or serving platter with lettuce. Add tomatoes, avocados, chicken, bacon and eggs.
2. Sprinkle cheese on top.
3. Drizzle with salad dressing and serve (see two dressing recipes below #9 and #10).

Tips:
-To prevent cut-up avocados from browning, immediately coat the pieces with fresh-squeezed lemon juice.

8. Mediterranean Tuna Salad:
Ingredients:
- 1 head butter or romaine lettuce, torn into bite-sized pieces
- ¼ pound (1 handful) green beans, steamed (optional)
- 1 cup grape tomatoes or 2 large tomatoes sliced
- 3 hard-boiled eggs, quartered
- ¼ cup Kalamata olives
- ¼ cup red onion, thinly sliced
- 1-2 five-ounce cans tuna, drained
- 1/3 cup organic vinaigrette or either of the below dressing recipes

Instructions:
1. Cover the bottom of a large bowl or platter with lettuce.
2. Add green beans, tomatoes and eggs. Sprinkle olives and onions on top and add tuna.
3. Drizzle with salad dressing and serve.

Tips:
-Pick the best organic tomatoes you can find and de- seed them.

9. Garlic Olive Oil Dressing:
Ingredients:
- ½ cup olive oil
- 5 cloves garlic minced, or better yet peeled and pressed
- 5 Tablespoons of Balsamic or Apple cider vinegar
- Dash of salt and pepper
- 1 teaspoon Italian herbs (optional)

Instructions:
1. Wisk all ingredients together and use as a salad dressing, dip for bread, drizzle for veggies, or marinade.

Tips:
-It is important to use fresh garlic and not out of a jar. Options: add a squirt of honey and/or Dijon mustard to dressing. Squeeze in ½ lemon to add a "zing."

10. <u>Olive Tapenade Dressing:</u>
Ingredients:
- ½ cup olive oil
- ¼ cup olive tapenade (in glass jar from grocery store)
- 4 Tablespoons of any vinegar – (I use Balsamic)

Instructions:
-Wisk tapenade, vinegar, olive oil and season with pepper.

11. <u>Best Spaghetti Sauce Ever:</u>
Ingredients:
- 2 Large cans of organic diced tomatoes
- 2 small cans of tomato paste
- 1 Large yellow onion chopped
- 6 Cloves garlic chopped
- 1 green and 1 red bell pepper chopped
- 1 small basket of mushrooms washed and sliced (optional)
- Olive Oil
- 1 Tbsp. of Italian herbs (and/or ½ cup fresh Italian parsley)
- 6 bay leaves,
- 3 Tablespoons of honey
- Hot sauce, salt, pepper (to taste)
- Optional- 1-pound sautéed grass-fed ground beef

Instructions:
1. Sauté veggies over medium/low heat in ¼ cup olive oil for 5 minutes.(sautéing is optional)
2. Put ingredients into a large pot, cook for 30-60 minutes.
3. Taste and add more seasonings as desired.

Tips:
-Serve sauce over zucchini spaghetti noodles or meatballs, or healthy pasta, and top with grated parmesan cheese.
-Serve with a green salad.
- For an easy FAST substitute, just get a bottle of good organic Marinara sauce, and add above veggies to spice it up!

12. <u>Simple Grilled Salmon and Veggies:</u>
Ingredients:
- 1 pound Wild caught salmon fillet cut into 4 pieces
- 1 zucchini halved length wise (optional)
- 2 red or green bell peppers halved and seeded
- 1 red onion cut into wedges
- 4 Tablespoons olive oil
- Salt and Pepper
- 1 lemon cut into 4 wedges

Instructions:
1. Heat grill to medium temperature.
2. Toss zucchini, peppers, and onion with 2 T olive oil and a dash of salt.
3. Sprinkle salmon with olive oil, pepper and salt.
4. Place vegetables and salmon in a grill pan. Or place Salmon directly on the grill and veggies on skewers.
5. Cook veggies 4 minutes per side.
6. Cook salmon, skin side down, without turning for 8 to 10 minutes (until it flakes with a fork).
7. Serve salmon with veggies and a wedge of lemon.

Tips:
-A green salad for a side dish with wild or cauliflower rice.
-Feel free to substitute veggies with asparagus, broccoli, squash.
-Optional: Top Salmon with Pesto or Aioli (recipe page 203).

13. <u>Eric's Grilled Chicken:</u>
Ingredients:
- 4-8 Chicken thighs or legs (organic) – rinsed and patted dry
- Olive oil
- Sea Salt and Ground Pepper
- Italian herbs (dry)

Instructions:

1. Trim off extra skin and fat from chicken. Drizzle with olive oil. Shake on salt, pepper, and Italian herbs.

2. Sear skin side of chicken on grill on medium heat for a few minutes. Careful not to blacken. Then *turn down flame,* and cook slowly on each side with lid closed for tasty BBQ flavor about 8 minutes per side, or until a knife pricked into chicken releases clear juice, not pink.

Tips:

-Slivers of fresh garlic under skin for a nice flavor.

-May serve with your favorite BBQ sauce on the side.

-May serve with green salad, wild rice, beets, guacamole, sauerkraut, cucumber or celery sticks with hummus. Yumm!

Snacks & Healthy Desserts

14. Healthier Decadent Chocolate Birthday Cake:

Ingredients:

- 1/3 cup 100% Maple syrup
- 1/3 cup honey
- 2 ¼ cups organic flour (I prefer part almond flour)
- 1/2 cup unsweetened cocoa powder (I use Ghirardelli)
- 1 cup organic mayonnaise (secret ingredient)
- 2 teaspoons baking soda
- 1 cup warm water
- 1½ teaspoons of pure vanilla extract

Instructions:

1. Wisk cocoa& hot water. Wisk in other wet ingredients.
2. Combine all dry ingredients, with a wisk or fork.
3. Combine wet and dry ingredients and mix just until blended, some lumps will remain.
4. Pour into greased 9 x 9 glass baking pan.
5. Bake at 350 degrees for 28 – 32 minutes. It is done when wood toothpick inserted in center comes out clean.
6. Remove from oven and cool completely.

Tips:
-The cake freezes well and tastes delicious when refrigerated or at room temperature. Use frosting recipe below.

15. Healthier Chocolate Frosting:
Ingredients:
- ½ cup butter (I prefer part butter and part coconut oil)
- 2 Tablespoons maple syrup (100% pure)
- 2 Tablespoons honey
- 3 Tablespoons unsweetened cocoa (I use Ghirardelli)
- 1 teaspoon vanilla (100% pure)

Instructions:
1. Blend all ingredients with an electric beater until well blended and fluffy. Frost cake once it has cooled.

16. Near Keto Pancakes:
Ingredients:
- 4 eggs
- ¼ cup oil (I prefer avocado, olive, or melted coconut)
- ¼ cup milk (any type)
- 1 Tablespoon maple syrup (100% pure organic)
- 2 teaspoons 100% vanilla extract
- 1 cup almond flour (fine)
- 1½ teaspoons baking *powder* (non-aluminum)

Instructions:
1. Mix all ingredients with a wisk or fork until combined.
2. Add more flour or milk as necessary. The batter should be like a thin cake batter.
3. Heat butter or ghee in a large frying pan (medium heat) and pour in 3 to 4 pancakes near edges.
4. Flip when bubbles appear on top, peek under to see that the pancake is lightly browned.
5. After both sides are brown, move to plate and make more.

Tips:
-You may add blueberries or dark chocolate chips to the top of each pancake before flipping. Serve with 100% maple syrup, butter, and/or berries.

17. <u>Near Keto Organic Reeses Peanut/Almond Butter Balls:</u>
Ingredients:
Filling:
- 1 cup organic peanut or almond butter (or half of each)
- 1/3 + cup of coconut flour or fine blanched almond flour
- 3 tablespoons maple syrup (100%)

Coating:
- 1 Tablespoon coconut oil
- 1 bag of dark chocolate chips (Lily's or Ghirardelli)
- 2 Tablespoons of pure maple syrup
- 1 teaspoon vanilla

Instructions:
1. Mix all filling ingredients together and freeze dough for 15 minutes.
2. Mold into 3/4 inch balls or egg shaped for Easter.
3. Place balls onto wax paper on cookie sheet.
4. Melt chocolate and coconut oil on low heat stirring a lot.
5. Remove from heat.
6. Add maple syrup and vanilla.
7. Drop a couple balls into the chocolate, and gently roll around with a small spoon.
8. Place balls on wax paper, drizzle extra chocolate over balls and chill for 20 minutes. Enjoy!

Tips:
-If dough is not thick enough you can add a little more flour.
-Keep them refrigerated!

18. Scrumptious Near Keto Granola:
Ingredients:
Dry:
- 4 cups rolled organic oats (uncooked oatmeal)
- 4 cups raw nuts and seeds (your choice of: walnuts, pecans, sunflower seeds, pumpkin seeds, flax seeds)
- 1 teaspoon sea salt
- 1 cup unsweetened thick shredded coconut(optional)

Wet:
- ¾ cup coconut oil
- ½ cup maple syrup (half honey is my preference)
- 3 teaspoons pure vanilla

Optional Ingredients:
- 1-2 cups *dried* currants, raisins, blueberries, cranberries, or dark chocolate chips

Instructions:
1. Melt coconut oil in saucepan on low if solid. Remove from heat, then add maple syrup, honey, and vanilla.
2. Combine all dry ingredients in large bowl except coconut, dried fruit and chocolate chips.
3. Pour wet ingredients over dry, mix until every oat and nut is coated. Pour mixture into 2-3 stainless cookie sheets with high edges (may use parchment paper).
4. Bake in a preheated oven at 350 degrees for 21 to 24 minutes total.
5. Take out halfway through toss, and add shredded coconut and dried fruit. Then press down hard with the back of a spatula in the pan (helps with clumping). Finish the baking time then remove from oven (granola should look lightly brown). It will keep crisping as it cools. Cool before enjoying. Sprinkle on the chocolate chips and break up gently leaving some in clumps. Enjoy!!!

Tips:
-You may cut the recipe in half and just use one big cookie pan.
-You may add 1-3 teaspoons cinnamon, or other dried fruits, nuts or seeds as you prefer.
-This is excellent for gifts and I usually freeze some.

19. Healthy Peach or Blueberry Crisp:
Filling Ingredients:
- 7 fresh peaches roughly chopped (Organic, or wash with vinegar water) or 5 cups blueberries-fresh or frozen,
- ¼ cup 100 % maple syrup or honey (or combination)
- 1 teaspoon vanilla
- ¼ cup flour (almond or coconut preferred)

Topping – Crumble Ingredients:
- 1 cup pecans or walnuts (rough chop)
- ¾ cup rolled oats (uncooked)
- ¼ cup maple syrup or honey (or combination)
- 5 Tablespoons coconut oil
- ½ cup flour (almond or coconut)

Instructions:
1. Preheat oven to 350 degrees.
2. Coat 8x8 or 9x9 glass pan or round glass pie pan with coconut or olive oil.
3. Mix filling ingredients and pour into glass pan.
4. Mix crumble ingredients with wooden spoon and add to top of fruit in an even layer.
5. Bake 38- 40 minutes until golden on top and fruit is bubbling.
6. Remove from oven and cool 10 minutes before serving.

Tips:
-Serve with whole fat Greek yogurt mixed with a spoon full of honey or maple syrup. -Have fun with this recipe.
-You can substitute any fruit including: strawberries, blueberries, raspberries, blackberries or apples.
-With peach or apple you may mix in ½ teaspoon cinnamon.

20. <u>Healthy Chewy Brownies:</u>
Ingredients:
- ¾ cup dark chocolate chips (I recommend Lily's brand)
- ¼ honey
- ¼ pure maple syrup
- 3 Tablespoons coconut oil
- 4 Tablespoons 100% almond butter or peanut butter
- 2 large eggs
- 1½ teaspoons vanilla
- 3 Tablespoons unsweetened cocoa powder
- 1 teaspoon baking soda
- 1 Cup Almond Flour (I recommend 1/3 of the cup coconut flour)
- 1 pinch sea salt

Instructions:
1. Grease 8 X 8-inch glass pan.
2. Preheat oven to 350 degrees.
3. Wisk together flour, cocoa powder, baking soda, and salt.
4. On low heat melt chocolate chips, oil, and almond butter. stirring constantly until a liquid.
5. Cool for 5 minutes.
6. Add honey, maple syrup and vanilla.
7. Wisk in eggs.
8. Then combine wet and dry ingredients until no lumps remain (it will be THICK). Pour in pan.
9. Bake 15-18 minutes. Dough will be "jiggly" still in the center. Remove from oven. Then with a paper towel press down the puffy edges so they will be chewy too.
10. Cool on counter for 30 minutes and then cool in fridge for 30 minutes.

Tips:
-May sprinkle with nuts before baking.
-Keeps in the fridge for a week, and 6 months in the freezer
-Another great brownie recipe is one made with dates. Just look
up: ***"Healthy Date Brownies."***

My Healthy Chewy Brownies recipe!

Index

214

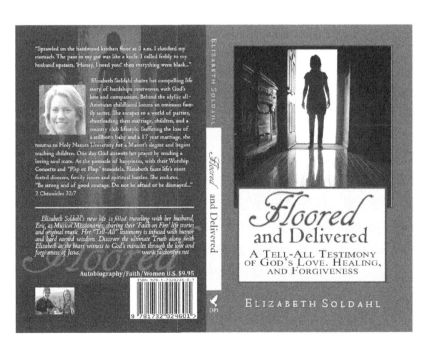

Find Elizabeth's #1 Testimonial Book on Amazon: 173202460X

217

Elizabeth's Recommended Healing Reading List:

1. *Floored and Delivered*, Elizabeth Soldahl -
2. New Spirit Filled Life Bible; KJV, New King James Version
3. *Chris Beat Cancer: A comprehensive Plan for Healing Naturally*, Chris Wark
4. *God's Way to Ultimate Health*, Malkmus & Dye
5. *From Hero to Zero and Redeemed*, Eric Soldahl
6. *Spiritual Firepower*, Eric Soldahl
7. *The Lord Who Heals You* ~ A study through the Bible App.
8. *The Truth about Cancer: What You Need to Know about Cancer's History, Treatment, and Prevention*, Ty M. Bollinger
9. *The Water Doctor*, Dr. Robert G. Logan with Elizabeth Logan Soldahl and Eric Soldahl -
10. *Water the Shocking Truth That Can Save Your Life* and *Bragg Healthy Lifestyle*, by Paul and Patricia Bragg
11. *Church, Again,* by Nolan Soldahl
12. *Powerful Inspirations*, by Kathy Ireland
13. *Dead Doctors Don't Lie*, Dr. Joel Wallach
14. *Unplanned*, Abby Johnson
15. *The Secrets to Deliverance*, Alexander Pagani
16. *Codependent No More: How to Stop Controlling Others and Start Caring for Yourself*, Melody Beattie
17. *Boundaries: When to Say Yes, How to Say No...*, John Townsend and Henry Cloud
18. *The Vaccine Friendly Plan*, Dr. Paul Thomas
19. *Deliverance Manual*, Gene B. Moody
20. *Relentless: Unleashing a Life of Purpose, Grit, and Faith*, John Tesh
21. *Dr. Steven Gundry's Books: The Plant Paradox Made Easy, The Longevity Paradox*
22. *Hope for the Perfectionist*, Dr. David Stoop
23. *Grace for Each Hour*, Mary Nelson ~ on Breast Cancer
24. *Every Woman's Guide To Natural Home Remedies*, Sally Freeman

Support Groups:

1. Celebrate Recovery (Christ centered recovery group for addictions/habits), Alcoholics Victorious, Overcomers Outreach.
2. Moms in Prayer
3. Hearts Being Healed Conferences
4. Stephen Ministry Training
5. Bible Study Fellowship
6. Christian Counseling

DVDs and CDs and TV shows:

1. Healing Praise CD ~ Gloria C. Ministries
2. Square One, Chris Beat Cancer, by Chris Wark
3. New Science of Epigenetics Proves DNA is Not Destiny ~ CBN News, Lorie Johnson
4. Starving Cancer: Ketogenic Diet – A Key to Recovery, CBN
5. Pastors to watch on TV or YouTube: John McArthur, Greg Laurie, and Billy or Franklin Graham, Charles Stanley, David Jeremiah, Perry Stone, Phillip Blair -Torch of Christ Ministries, and Rabbi Schneider – Discovering the Jewish Jesus.
6. Focus on the Family – Dr. James Dobson, videos, books, radio.
7. Cancer the Forbidden Cure – Movie/Documentary – YouTube
8. "Dr. Lorraine Day Cancer Cure," on YouTube
9. Documentary – *Vaxxed*

Acknowledgments:

Eric Soldahl, Laura Tate Anderson, Pastor George Tate, Grace Bahu, Courtney Artiste, My Parents: Robert and Mary Ellen Logan, Florence Soldahl, Daughters: Jennifer, Kate, Amber. Sons: Grayson, Nolan and Paul, Brothers: Mark and Don. Nancy Hertzog, Jerolyn Soldahl, Robynn Coulter, Jamelle DeWeese, Kimberley Woods, Heather Bowers, Dolores Heaton, Noble and Sharlene Spees, Danette Varga, Krystal Sautter, Mike and Tiffany Burson, Keven Campbell, Laurel and Art at Cornerstone Music, Johanna Vanderpool, Penny Roberts King, Bonnie Moody, Kim Vinson, Emily Pappas, Dr. Lorraine Day, Mary Beth Pollard, June Brooke, Phil and Krista Fuller, Sarah Tinsley, Sharlene Clark, Kathleen Aubereg, Melody and Mitch Forster, Kathy Ireland, John Tesh, Connie Sellecca, Joni Eareckson Tada, Chip and Joanna Gaines, Keith and Kristyn Getty, Pastor Duncan, Lenny Gerardo, Dr. Steven Gundry, Sarah Chastain, Carolyn Lustfeild, Amanda Taylor, Pastor Barry and Jean Dilworth, Terrie Olson, Jean Nation, Laurynda Marques, Jamie and Chrissy Duncan, Luba Mitsuk, Hope Gallup, Pastor Curtis Leins, Sue Parkins, Brad, Jessica and Parker Finley, Paul and Patricia Bragg, Chris Wark, Mike Huckabee, Debbie and Ken McMaster, Marion Knox, Christopher Melton, Krissy Richardson, Joanne Kerr, Olivia Angeli, Dr. Godby, Karen and Rich Eddy, Steve Duerson, Nita Hansen.

For more information on Elizabeth and Eric's Musical Missionary Ministry go to: www.Faithonfire.net

Order Books on Amazon.com

If this book was meaningful to you, please consider posting a review. *Direct Link:* **www.amazon.com/dp/1732024685**

What Readers are Saying:

"A compelling story of healing and faith, with a treasure trove of practical health information. Including delicious recipes!"
Laura Tate Anderson, M.S.

"Consider this Book for your Next Group Bible Study or for a Personal Devotional." Steven D.

*****FIVE STARS! *"This book will give you hope. A MUST READ if you, or someone you love, has received a cancer diagnosis. Provides a path to healing that modern medicine does not offer."*
Carrie B.

"If you read, Chicken Soup for the Soul, or Chris Beat Cancer, you will love Liz Lives, Healed with God's Word and His Food!" Eric

"This book will bring many people to a deeper knowledge of God's healing power through Jesus Christ!" C. Grace

"I'm going to keep this handy as a "reference book" and buy several copies for friends and relatives." LAS

"I'm reading it twice and 'marking it up!' Has the BEST tips to avoid deadly disease and to stay healthy. I suggest you: READ THIS BOOK!"

Made in the USA
Columbia, SC
23 November 2020

25256040R00124